KU-331-621

Minister for Health and Children's Foreword

I am very pleased to publish *Your Views about Health* – the Report on Consultation for the Health Strategy *Quality and Fairness – a Health System for You.*

From the outset I decided that the approach to preparing the Health Strategy would be based on consultation and participation with all the stakeholders: members of the public, statutory and voluntary organisations, health boards and their staff, and staff in my own Department. An extensive consultation process was undertaken and its findings are set out in detail in this report. Indeed the response from the public and organisations greatly exceeded our expectations and provides extremely valuable insights into the issues that need to be addressed.

I would like to take this opportunity to thank everyone who gave so willingly of their time and energy to make a submission and to contribute to making the consultation process a success. The contents of the Strategy reflect the key themes which emerged from the consultation process. In my view, this is what will make the Strategy robust and durable because it is based on what you have said to us. By any standards, the Strategy is an ambitious programme of reform and strategic change and it is important that it has been built on such strong foundations.

Micheál Martin

Micheál Martin, T.D.
Minister for Health and Children

HS 362·1 YOUR

Your Views about Health

Report on Consultation

Quality and Fairness - A Health System for You
Health Strategy

DONATIONS
- 8 AUG 2005
UCC LIBRARY

**DEPARTMENT
OF HEALTH AND
CHILDREN**
AN ROINN
SLÁINTE AGUS LEANAÍ

HEALTH SCIENCES BROOKFIELD
LIBRARY
CORK

Table of Contents

Introduction

• Health Strategy *Quality and Fairness – A Health System for You*   3

• Consultation process   4

• Expectations for the Strategy   8

Part 1 Views and proposals from the general public   10

Part 2 Views and proposals from organisations   50

Part 3 Views and proposals from health boards   114

Part 4 Views and proposals from staff of the Department of Health and Children   130

Part 5 Report on the National Anti-Poverty Strategy consultation process   136

Part 6 Key themes emerging from the consultation process   150

Appendices

Appendix 1 Members of Project Team Consultation Sub-Group and
Health Board Co-ordinators   157

Appendix 2 The consultation pack *Your Views about Health*   159

Appendix 3 List of contributors (organisations)   167

Report by Anne Colgan, Colgan & Associates and Dr. Jean Tubridy

Introduction

Health Strategy
Quality and Fairness - A Health System for You

Why a new Strategy?

The purpose of the Health Strategy is to improve the health of people living in Ireland and to develop, reform and modernise health and personal social services over the next 7 to 10 years. It builds on *Shaping a Healthier Future*, which was published in 1994 as a strategy for effective healthcare in the 1990s.

Vision and guiding principles

The vision for the future of the health system in Ireland is described in the Health Strategy, *Quality and Fairness – A Health System for You* as follows:

* *A health system that supports and empowers you, your family and community to achieve your full health potential*

* *A health system that is there when you need it, that is fair and that you can trust*

* *A health system that encourages you to have your say, listens to you, and ensures that your views are taken into account.*

Four principles guided the development of the Strategy. These principles are **equity, people-centredness, quality** and **accountability.**

Structures for preparing the Strategy

A number of structures were set up to prepare the Strategy. The preparation was overseen by a Steering Group representing the Department of Health and Children, the Department of the Taoiseach, the Department of Finance and the health boards. The Steering Group had overall responsibility for the consultation process.

A Project Team comprising officials of the Department of Health and Children and the health boards was established to work to the Steering Group and produce the Strategy document. A sub-group of the Project Team worked with external consultants in designing, planning and implementing the consultation process.

The Minister established a National Health Strategy Consultative Forum representative of key stakeholders to support the Steering Group by providing advice on the key themes and direction of the Strategy and on the process for its preparation. It was a valuable forum for discussion and underpinned the entire consultation process.

In addition to the plenary sessions, the Forum was divided into eight working groups to deal with specific issues: funding, eligibility, delivery systems/human resources, population health, quality, voluntary/statutory interface, e-health and futures in healthcare. These mirrored working groups established within the Department of Health and Children.

The Working Group on the National Anti-Poverty Strategy (NAPS) and Health was set up in Autumn 2000 to set targets for the reduction of health inequalities among people who are poor or socially excluded, as part of the overall strategy to address poverty. The NAPS health targets and the framework for achieving these targets are an important strand in the Health Strategy.

The Working Group undertook a major consultation process that has fed in to the preparation of the Health Strategy.

Consultation process

Planning the consultation process

From the outset, it was decided by the Minister for Health and Children, Mr Micheál Martin T.D., that the approach to preparing the Health Strategy should be a strongly participative one. Referring to the importance of a shared vision of the future of the health services, he stated that "successful change…must be based on effective consultation and participation by all concerned".

Consultants were appointed in early February, 2001 charged with designing, planning, implementing and reporting on the consultation programme. The consultants, Colgan and Associates, undertook this work under the direction of the Steering Group and worked directly with the Consultation Sub-Group of the Project Team (Appendix 1).

The brief given to the consultants was to plan, implement and complete the consultation process so as to feed into the preparation of the Strategy by mid-year. This timescale was an important determinant of the scope of the consultation and of the target times for completing each phase of the consultation process. An intensive planning process took place during February and early March. Consultations began at the end of March and the main programme of work was undertaken during April and May.

Consulting the stakeholders

The main objective of the consultation process was to gather the views of members of the public, service users, service providers, staff, management and governance of the health services and to channel these views into the development of the Health Strategy.

The National Health Strategy Consultative Forum

A central part of the consultation process took place through the work of the National Health Strategy Consultative Forum which is described above.

Members of the general public

The main means of consulting with the general public was through the consultation pack *Your Views about Health*. It had been the Minister's wish that local and regional consultation meetings would take place where the general public could come together to discuss issues and concerns about health and health services. However, these meetings did not take place on account of the restrictions on meetings and travel put in place to prevent the spread of foot-and-mouth disease.

Individuals and organisations were invited to express their views about the future of the health system in the form of written responses to a number of questions. *Your Views About Health* provided background information on the Health Strategy and on the range of health services provided at present (Appendix 2). People were invited to describe their experiences of the health services and to give their views on future change. This public consultation process was widely advertised and promoted at national and local level.

Individuals and groups with special health needs

There are many groups of people whose concerns arise out of their particular circumstances and experiences. The groups in question include people with disabilities, children and young people, older people and people who are marginalised or disadvantaged by the circumstances of their lives.

Consultation with these groups was undertaken through the various representative groups and organisations that work with and represent the views, needs and issues of the people concerned. This consultation took a number of forms:

- Involvement of representative groups on the National Health Strategy Consultative Forum

- Input from the group or organisation through the consultation pack *Your Views about Health*

- Participation in service user/service provider forums arranged in some health boards.

The Minister also wrote to national representative bodies working in the Community and Voluntary Sector inviting them to undertake consultation with the groups whose interests they represent.

People experiencing poverty

In the case of people experiencing poverty, a separate consultation process was undertaken through the National Anti-Poverty Strategy.

The National Anti-Poverty Strategy (NAPS) was published in 1997. It originated from a Government commitment to the development of an anti-poverty strategy at the UN World Social Summit in Copenhagen in 1995.

Under the Programme for Prosperity and Fairness (PPF), the NAPS is being reviewed and new targets will be set in 'health' and 'accommodation/housing' while targets in the other areas are being revised. The commitment in the PPF to set NAPS targets for health was particularly timely for the Health Strategy which has equity as one of its key principles. It was intended from the outset that the NAPS health targets and associated monitoring and implementation framework would form an important strand in the Strategy.

To progress the issue of setting NAPS targets for health, the Department of Health and Children established a Working Group on NAPS and Health in Autumn 2000. The NAPS Working Group embarked on a wide-ranging consultation, designed and managed by the Institute for Public Health. The outcome of this consultation process fed directly into the work on the Health Strategy.

Organisations

A variety of opportunities were offered to organisations through which they could contribute to the development of the Strategy:

- National organisations participated in the work of the National Health Strategy Consultative Forum

- National and local organisations contributed written views and proposals through the consultation pack *Your Views about Health*

- A wide range of national organisations and bodies were invited by the Minister for Health and Children to submit views

- A number of health boards organised workshops for locally-based organisations.

Staff, management and governing bodies in the health services

A range of consultation processes were provided for people involved in the health services.

Health board and health agency consultations

Extensive and detailed consultation was undertaken in each of the ten health board areas. Generally, the consultation took place at several levels, including staff, management and governance (health board members). Health service staff were also encouraged to take advantage of the public consultation process as individuals and many took up that invitation. The consultation process was led in each board by a senior officer, nominated by the Chief Executive Officer (Appendix 1).

In a number of locations, Partnership Committees, which work under the auspices of the Health Services National Partnership Forum, undertook consultation projects with staff in their agencies, as well as working on the overall consultation plan with the health board co-ordinators.

Consultation with staff in the Department of Health and Children

Staff of the Department of Health and Children participated in a series of facilitated workshops which were designed and managed by the Institute of Public Administration.

Market research

As part of the consultation process, the Department of Health and Children commissioned Irish Marketing Surveys to carry out market research. The purpose of the research was to gather qualitative and quantitative data on public views about health and health services, based on a scientifically drawn sample of members of the public. The particular objectives of the research were the following:

- To establish the general public's views about health

- To understand the public's views of their own health and to gauge basic health/safety behaviours

- To understand the public's views of and satisfaction with the delivery of various health services

- To identify changes needed to improve health and well-being in Ireland, both in terms of behavioural or attitudinal changes needed among the general public as well as changes needed to the health services/system.

The research was carried out in April and May, 2001. The report is available on www.doh.ie or from the Department of Health and Children.

Responses to the consultation process

There was an excellent response to each strand of the consultation process. **1512** submissions were received from members of the public and over **300** submissions were received from organisations.

The expectation that the views expressed through the consultation process will have influence are typified by the following comment:

> *The consultative process is a positive development, it is important that these views are incorporated in the Strategy for it to have real meaning on the ground.*

The welcome for the consultation was, on occasion, tinged with some cynicism. For example:

> *Enclosed are some of the Consultation Forms from parents at pre-school. We have 20 parents here but a lot of parents were cynical of filling in the form. They are very angry with the Health Service.*

Links with the development of the Strategy

The submissions contributed to the development of the Health Strategy in a number of ways:

- The material in submissions was indexed and made available to the working groups developing the Strategy

- More detailed reports on the content of submissions on a particular theme were provided on request

- Reports on the content of submissions were made to the Steering Group

- An overview of the findings was provided to the National Health Strategy Consultative Forum at a conference in July, 2001.

This report

This report gives an account of the views and proposals coming through from each strand of the consultation process.

The structure of the report is as follows:

Part 1   Views and proposals from members of the public

Part 2   Views and proposals from organisations

Part 3   Views and proposals from health boards (consolidated from the reports on each health board consultation)

Part 4   Views and proposals from staff of the Department of Health and Children (based on a report prepared by the Institute of Public Administration)

Part 5   Report of the consultation process undertaken by the Working Group on the National Anti-Poverty Strategy (NAPS) and Health (prepared by the Institute for Public Health)

Part 6   Key themes emerging from the consultation process.

Expectations for the Health Strategy

Many members of the public, as well as organisations and health service personnel, spoke about their expectations for the Health Strategy. Many located these expectations in the wider context of Irish society today and the challenges and opportunities we face in looking to the future of our health system.

The Health Strategy is seen as offering the opportunity to make a significant difference to the quality of life of people living in this country. People point out that while resources are now available to a greater extent than heretofore, money, in itself, is not the complete answer. It is argued that vision, strategic thinking, research-based planning and a holistic approach are essential if the Strategy is to have an impact.

People have a strong expectation that the Strategy will mean real change. These comments from members of the public highlight the feelings expressed:

> *People's health is the most important thing and it should be a basic right to have that taken care of and to have confidence that all that can be done for your health is being done.*

> *I would like that the new Health Strategy will not be a 'talking shop.' As far as strategy is concerned, get started and do something. Loads of paperwork won't reduce the waiting lists.*

> *I am very glad it is coming as it is long overdue but I hope it will go into action and not left on the shelf.*

Similarly, many organisations, when welcoming the new Strategy, underline the importance of an implementation programme. They see explicit short-term and long-term targets as essential to an effective implementation process and have also proposed a range of monitoring mechanisms, which should reflect commitment to partnership with all the key stakeholders.

Challenges and opportunities

The submissions underline the importance of the contexts in which this Health Strategy is being developed. Some facets of the social and economic landscape in modern Ireland offer opportunities for real change; others pose major challenges.

The impact of the changing demographic structure of the population is raised by several contributors. The increasing population and in particular, the increasing proportion of older people, will make new and substantial demands on health services and will create a need for new kinds of service.

The increasingly multicultural society and, especially, the growing numbers of refugees and asylum seekers require new responses geared to the needs of these groups.

While our improved economic performance offers possibilities for increased investment in health services, many groups and individuals are clear that there are increasingly serious inequalities in society. Many marginalised groups are growing in number, for example, homeless people and young people at risk of suicide. These groups need special attention in the Health Strategy.

New technological developments are seen as offering valuable opportunities to improve both the delivery and administration of healthcare systems in Ireland.

A rise in client expectations was highlighted by the submissions. This trend is described in the submission from the Institute of Public Administration's Health Sector Advisory Group:

> *The development of the health services in Ireland is being shaped increasingly by an articulate, generally well-educated and discerning public. The requirements of the public are influenced both by their individual needs and also by a culture which demands a high quality, responsive, accessible service.*

It is argued that, in common with other countries in Western Europe, healthcare costs are rising at a greater rate than the cost of living. Two factors are identified as contributing to this:

- The cost of indemnity cover

- Growing administrative costs in increasingly complex healthcare systems.

A number of submissions commenting on the healthcare system in Ireland as compared with its international counterparts are critical of our comparative status in relation to life expectancy for those who have reached 60 years, premature death rates, death rates from coronary heart disease, number of hospital beds per capita and the endemic problem of waiting lists.

The past and present state of the health services is seen as posing a major challenge to the Health Strategy.

PART 1

Views and proposals from the general public

Introduction 11

Chapter 1: Meeting special needs 13

Chapter 2: Community health and personal social services 21

Chapter 3: Hospital services 25

Chapter 4: Health education, health promotion and illness prevention 29

Chapter 5: Equality, equity, entitlements 34

Chapter 6: Quality and accountability systems 37

Chapter 7: People's experiences of the health services 39

Introduction

Consulting the general public

The consultation process

The main means of consulting the general public was through the use of a consultation pack *Your Views about Health* which gave background information on the Health Strategy and on the range of health services provided at present (Appendix 2). It invited members of the general public to describe their experiences of the health services, both positive and negative, and to make proposals about ways of promoting and enhancing the health of the nation. There was a focus on health and well-being, rather than on health services alone. The questions also contained an invitation to think strategically, by inviting people to prioritise their most important change proposals.

Valuable help in designing a 'user-friendly' consultation process was gained from members of the public who took part in focus groups in Dublin, Navan, Waterford and Limerick.

The analysis of submissions

An outline framework for capturing the key themes and proposals in submissions was developed with the Consultation Sub-Group of the Project Team, taking account of the key strategic issues emerging in developing the Health Strategy.

It was subsequently adjusted to take account of the main areas of concern to the public. All submissions were read and coded, using the framework. The proposals and issues in each submission were entered on a database. This material was then drawn together, under the framework headings and a report on the main findings was prepared.

The respondents

1512 responses were received from individuals and families. Of those who specified their age group (1284), 58 per cent were aged between 30 and 59 years. A further 18 per cent were over 60 years, while a small percentage (9 per cent) were under 30 years old.

Among those respondents who indicated their gender (1314), more than two-thirds (68 per cent) were female and 19 per cent were male. There was a good balance between urban and rural respondents. Of those who gave information about their location (1300), 46 per cent were from an urban area and 40 per cent were from a rural area.

HEALTH SCIENCES BROOKFIELD LIBRARY CORK

Reporting on the consultation findings

More than 10,000 separate change proposals and suggestions were received in response to the questions. There were strong common themes and consensus on many issues. There were also views on matters that may only affect a minority of people, but for whom the issue is of great importance, for example, a rare condition or disability.

Table 1 gives a breakdown of the ranking of proposals and the main themes.

Table 1: **Key areas of change proposed in submissions from general public:**

Proposed change area	Percentage of proposals on each area
Meeting special needs	23%
Community services	18%
Acute hospital services	15%
Health promotion	13%
Equity, eligibility and entitlements	10%
Quality systems	7%
Improving people's experience of health services	5%
Other	9%
Total	**100%**

The significant overlap between the themes and issues raised suggested several possible ways of organising the material. For example, the proposals relating to older people and people with disabilities are equally relevant to the topics of community care and acute services. The method of organising the information was chosen with a view to optimising its usefulness to the reader and its linkages with the themes in the Health Strategy. Accordingly the analysis and report are thematic, rather than quantitative. An overview of widely-held views is given. Attention is also drawn to minority concerns.

Extracts from individual submissions are given, where the direct words used by individuals are very potent in expressing the richness and diversity of ideas and feelings and in giving a clear sense of the intent of the contributor.

Chapter 1

Meeting special needs

Introduction

Almost a quarter (23 per cent) of the proposals made by members of the public concerned better ways of meeting the special health and personal social service needs of particular groups. The needs of older people emerged as a very high priority. A good deal of attention was paid also to the needs of people with disabilities, including people with chronic illnesses. A common theme running though the proposals in respect of each of these groups was the need for more support for carers.

This chapter sets out proposals from the general public for meeting the needs of:

1.1 Older people

1.2 People with mental health difficulties

1.3 People with learning difficulties

1.4 People with physical and sensory disabilities and chronic illnesses

1.5 Other groups with special needs

1.1 **Older people**

There were some clear trends in the material concerning older people and their health needs and these can be summarised as follows:

- Older people should be able to remain in their own homes and in their own communities for as long as they can

- State support must be put in place to make this possible

- The quality of life and the quality of care for older people at home must be of the highest standard

- The quality of life of family carers must be supported. Their lives should not be impoverished or diminished as a result of choosing to care for an older family member

- It is to the mutual advantage of the older person, the family and the State for the State to invest in enabling people to stay in their homes and communities

- People should be able to access services when and where they need them

- There should be a flexible continuum of service – people should not be forced to opt for either residential care or home care, when they want a 'mix' of both

- Service delivery to older people needs to be underpinned by an attitude of respect for the status, contribution and dignity of the older person

- The context of family life is changing and these changes need to be reflected in policy and services; there are many pressures on families and family carers that did not apply in the past.

Support for family carers

There were many calls for a formal strategy with specific targets and goals for family carers. This should cover support services, respite services, training, emotional support, peer support and financial support.

The need for financial support for family carers figured very strongly in the submissions. People argued that there are significant costs associated with caring and that these need to be recognised.

Among the proposals made were the following:

- A standardised national assessment for the Carer's Allowance

- Broader criteria for the Carer's Allowance

- Removal of the means test for the Carer's Allowance.

While many people spoke about financial support, there was emphasis also on the need for other kinds of help. People spoke about quite simple things that would help them to manage. For example, one person said that access to a washing machine would be a great help in caring for their older relative; others made the case for more help with the costs of heating or improved fuel allowance.

A proposal was made for the inclusion of a question in the national census to establish the extent of 'hidden' caring and the time being devoted to it.

Community support services

A comprehensive range of community-based support services is needed to enable older people to have the best possible quality of life. People want improved levels of service, involving more key personnel 'on the ground', and they want services delivered in ways that are more responsive to their needs.

A consistent theme was that of bringing the services to the older person, for example through more home visiting by medical personnel and having more screening and testing facilities such as hearing tests available locally. The issue of local transport, particularly in rural areas, was seen as a major barrier to accessing services. Over and over, people pointed to the difficulty for older people in getting to clinics and appointments when they do not have private transport.

The following listing describes the range of improvements people wish to see in community-based services:

Personal supports

- More home help hours, with greater flexibility to work at weekends and evenings

- Flexible respite, in-home and out-of-home

- Respite for older couples

- Purpose-built day centres, with high quality activities and medical services

- Sheltered housing

- Alarm systems with free maintenance

- Higher levels of monitoring

- More support for voluntary groups working with older people

- Easier access to aids and appliances

- Cut in waiting times to have grant applications processed, for example, grants for adapted housing

- Delivery of continence sheets to homes

- Emergency 'drop-in' facilities where a carer could bring a family member

- Extended meals-on-wheels services.

Besides purposeful visiting by nurses, doctors and therapists, there was an emphasis on visiting as an essential service in its own right. There were suggestions for the setting up of 'formal' schemes of informal visiting, for example, drawing on young people, or other people in a community, or a 'community mothers' type scheme, or a version of the home help scheme.

Medical supports

Among the medical supports people wished to see improved or developed were the following:

- Home nursing for older people who are ill

- Community nursing

- Geriatrician care and access to regular geriatric review

- Special doctors for older people

- Visiting occupational therapists and physiotherapists

- Community hospitals with respite beds and accident and emergency (A&E) facilities for older people.

Residential care

While most submissions focused on the need to develop community-based care as the top priority, people saw the need for a continuum of care, of which residential care is a critical element.

The main proposals made in relation to residential care were:

- More places provided at low or no cost by the State

- Cheaper private care/higher subsidy

- Enhanced quality of care within residential services.

Many people felt that it is unfair for older people who have paid tax and PRSI all their working lives to have to pay for nursing home care. Some felt that health boards should be much more involved in provision.

Some older people expressed fears about not being able to afford care. Others didn't want to be dependent on their adult children to pay for their care.

In relation to the quality of residential care, some of the proposals were for very simple and basic facilities:

- More stimulus for institutionalised people

- More activity other than watching TV

- Large print and talking books

- Outings and holidays

- Visits from the social worker

- Occupational therapy.

Higher levels of monitoring of residential services were proposed in a number of submissions.

Respect

Many people wrote about the importance of respect for older people. There was a view that older people are often in awe of service providers. The need for an advocacy service for older people was mentioned many times. People spoke about the need for campaigns to raise awareness about conditions such as Alzheimer's disease and campaigns to combat ageism.

People said...

Employ people to help [older people] at meal times in hospitals. I saw this in (named hospital). Very nice food left on a big table, with elderly patients, some after a stroke, some very weak and not able to cut up their food or butter their bread or open jam or marmalade. Please could someone be employed to help these people with their meals.

*In [named hospital] the tray was left, the patient was weak and could not pour out her pot of tea, I a visitor helped her with her meal. **(Female, 50-59, urban)***

*I have found no co-ordination in services for the old, you are just passed from one office to another. Anything I have learned about e.g entitlements for my mother, has been through 'word of mouth' from other carers. **(Female, 40-49, urban)***

*Incontinence sheets should be delivered to the person's home. The nurse used to bring them but does not do so now. It is difficult for a person who is living alone to get someone to collect them. **(Female, over 70, rural)***

*Many relatives leave their professions to take care of elderly relatives and find themselves isolated, no social life and house-bound. **(Female, 50-59, rural)***

*At times the elderly are treated like children or as though they are intellectually impaired. For example, treatment, test results, diagnoses etc are not given to them so they are in a state of fear as to what is actually wrong with them and what will happen. **(Female, 40-49, urban)***

*Kindness to all old people, even if they behave a bit awkward. **(Male, over 70, rural)***

*I live in sheltered housing which is excellent and I am very lucky. When I came here twelve years ago, our public health nurse called one day each week to everyone's door, which was very reassuring. Now I do not know the current person and have requested a non-urgent visit –I do not blame her but the system – she has a huge area to cover with many senior citizens. I have looked after my health and so far continue to be independent, TG, which will be a help in the battle ahead. Diet is very important for senior citizens and those who do not bother to eat sensibly go downhill very quickly. I see it all around me. Perhaps you could take note. **(Female, over 70, urban)***

1.2 **People with mental health difficulties**

The needs of people with mental health problems got more attention in submissions than other conditions. Again, the emphasis was on support and treatment in the community. The range of proposals about community-based services included the following:

- Training for GPs to help them to meet the needs of people with mental health problems

- A doctor with skills in mental health to work alongside GPs

- A psychiatrist should attend monthly at local community centres

- More emphasis on counselling

- Teams to support people experiencing post-traumatic stress

- Respite for families of people with chronic mental health conditions

- Mental health services geared to the needs of adolescents and young people

- Much more investment in child psychological and counselling services - poor follow-up after diagnosis, so problems grow and get out of hand

- Much more follow-up and support after discharge from a psychiatric hospital

- More support following a move from long-stay to community setting.

Several proposals were made for the setting up of an advocacy service for people with mental health problems. For those in residential settings, there were proposals for better levels of activity and more therapeutic care. There was also much concern about growing levels of suicide in Ireland.

1.3 **People with learning difficulties**

Proposals about the health needs of people with learning difficulties called for more family support, carer support, community services, disability awareness and campaigns to dispel prejudice.

The needs of carers of adults with learning difficulties were raised. Here again, a non-means tested carer's allowance was proposed, as well as whole-family counselling, respite and linked support services. It was suggested that no one over 60 years should be expected to provide care, on their own, for an adult relative with a learning disability.

The proposals made included the following:

- At least one staff member in each residential setting should have a role and training to listen, communicate and resolve conflict. Parents and families should always be consulted about decisions affecting their relative with a learning difficulty

- Hospital services should be available which are geared to the needs of people with a severe mental handicap

- Greater levels of awareness are needed among health service staff about hidden disabilities such as Attention Deficit Disorder (ADD)

- Friendship groups for young people should be supported.

1.4 **People with physical and sensory disabilities and chronic illnesses**

As with other disabilities, the submissions make the case for greater community support for people with physical and sensory disabilities.

Among the proposals were:

- Improved detection of disability, including hearing impairment, in infants and children

- Improved transport provision for people who have mobility impairments, including older people

- Better supports for deaf people attending hospitals, clinics and other health services.

Several submissions were concerned about people with particular chronic conditions. The need for local clinics for Myalgic Encephalomyelitis (ME) sufferers was raised, as well as the need for formal recognition of ME as a disability. It was proposed that ME should be included in the World Health Organisation classification of impairments and disabilities. People suffering from lymphodoema want more medical and financial support for their condition, as well as greater awareness of its implications.

According to submissions, there are huge gaps in services for young people with chronic conditions. Gaps were identified in community, hospital and residential care services.

A small number of contributors described in some detail the severe problems they experienced in getting support, services, treatment and basic understanding for the condition of gender dysphoria. The people concerned have found that many years elapsed before they were able to get a diagnosis and that, even then, only very limited treatment facilities were available, in spite of EU directives.

1.5 **Other groups with special needs**

The need for health services geared to meeting the particular health needs of both men and women was highlighted.

Strategies are needed also to protect the interests of both women and men who experience violence in the home. There were proposals about the need to protect children at risk of being abused, as well as more care for those who have experienced abuse.

Only a few submissions focused specifically on the needs of disadvantaged minorities. There were some concerns about good service provision for refugees and asylum seekers, Travellers and people living in very disadvantaged communities. There was a proposal for school meals, to ensure good nutrition for children who may not have nutritious food at home.

People said...

*Suicide is increasing so much on this island, it needs to be addressed a lot…I'm aware certain measures have been implemented – we need to do something on a grand scale to prevent the pain and sadness that's very much part of life here, especially in rural communities. **(Female, 40-49, urban)***

Improve mental health services. This service needs to actually work the hours other medical staff work and to be more flexible – more psychiatric nurses who could visit people at home e.g the elderly and very young. **(Female, 50-59, urban)**

*General practitioners should have a thorough understanding of what people with psychiatric problems have to endure and not regard them as hypochondriacs…When psychiatric patients are discharged from hospital, their progress [or lack of progress] should be monitored. At present, I have no-one in whom I can confide. **(Male, 50-59, rural)***

*Lets make our mothers and fathers of teenage children and early twenties more aware of the emotional support that young adults need. Are there signs we can watch for? It's not just the depressed child that commits suicide it can also be the smiling child/adult. **(Anon)***

*There was no counselling [for ME] available on the medical card even though I was extremely depressed. I found out, by chance, of a charity-based counselling service, but this is something that many people would not know about or it would not be available in many areas. **(Female, 20-29, urban)***

*As my lymphodoema is primary I have learned to live with it. But for those women and men who suffer lymphodoema as a result of surgery for their cancer, it would break your heart that they get no assistance to help them either with bandaging and surgical appliances for arms and legs. They also need encouragement to help them cope with these swellings as well as their cancer…we [other sufferers] would love to try to help them to understand their problem. Health boards should encourage support groups and GPs should have a directory of same. **(Female, 50-59, rural)***

*My disabled son was moved from the institution which had been his home for 9 years without consultation, while I, his mother, was out of the country. I feel this was deliberate. **(Female, 30-39, urban)***

*Can you please provide pre-school facilities [in North Dublin area] possibly attached to national schools, with special needs teachers, etc for children like D. Can you please provide extra support for us, guidance, advice etc…Please help us. I would not be sending you this, but I am desperate for help for D. Thank you for taking the time to read this. **(Parent of 3-year-old boy with autism)***

The services for disability are in disarray. They are inadequately funded and they are very poorly co-ordinated. There are a large number of voluntary bodies that have provided fragmented services to the best of their ability and there is urgent need to organise the structure of these services so they can become seamless. For example there is no screening for hearing loss in the newborn period, not even for high risk groups and there are no facilities to test the under fives adequately. Many of the children with physical disabilities have to travel long distances for services to Dublin. **(Consultant Paediatrician)**

*I am a person suffering with a mental health difficulty and a consumer of psychiatric services for a number of years. Up till recently I was residing in Dublin. I found the Dublin services far from satisfactory. Hospitalisations seemed to be overlong for what purpose I remain unsure. Follow-up care was very hit and miss. Your doctor and hospital is based on what catchment area you reside in and if you find you can't relate to your appointed doctor unless you can afford private care you may find it difficult to feel confident about your care. Since moving to Kildare I find the follow-up care to be far superior and the doctor to be more open to client input to care. Whether this is down to the doctor or the area I remain unsure. **(Female, 30-39, urban)***

Chapter 2

Community health and personal social services

Introduction

Improvements in community health and personal social services were the subject of almost 2000 proposals and accounted for 18 per cent of all proposals.

The core theme running through the proposals was the need for a huge increase in the level of services delivered in the community and a much more flexible approach to the delivery of services. People want services to be provided as close as possible to their own local area. The business of travelling to services is a cause of concern and annoyance, especially in rural areas where there are gaps in public transport. Services should be provided when people need them. This will mean that services will have to be available outside standard working hours, at weekends and holidays.

People are looking for an extended range of local services. They want more access to complementary therapy, more diagnostic services provided by GPs, and local community hospitals that can offer day services such as respite for older people in the community.

Where people must travel to out-patient clinics outside their area, the lack of transport comes up regularly as a barrier and an inconvenience. The possibility that services could be brought to the people through mobile clinics and outreach services, rather than having the people always go to the service, is raised in submissions. Concerns about access to services in remote rural areas and on the islands were raised by several contributors.

In summary, then, the top priorities for change and improvement were:

- More community-based services and community health professionals

- Improved access to complementary medicine

- Improved GP services

- Better linkages between services.

Community-based services and community health professionals

The main areas where people want to see improvements in the level of service in the community were:

- Community nursing

- Health centres

- More therapists

- Local testing and screening e.g. eyes, hearing, blood pressure, bone density

- Helplines and advice for minor health problems and advice as to whether GP or hospital visit is needed

- Community-based counselling

- Community hospitals

- Local transport.

Submissions also commented on the need for significantly improved dental and orthodontic services, greater family support, improved ambulance services, domiciliary midwifery services and family planning services in rural areas.

One contributor who is professionally involved in midwifery teaching proposed that midwifery is an important form of health promotion and should have a visible presence within the community setting. She also proposed changes to the Maternity and Infant Care Scheme, to include midwives as maternity carers, thus providing greater choice to women.

Complementary medicine and therapy

There was a good deal of interest in the area of complementary medicine and complementary therapies. People are concerned about their right to have choice and access to remedies other than conventional drugs. There were many calls for less reliance on these drugs and more use of homeopathic and natural remedies.

People want to have this choice alongside the choice of traditional medicine. Among the many points made are the following:

- Complementary medicine should be available in doctors' surgeries

- People need more information about alternative treatments

- GPs should know about local availability of complementary practitioners and should refer patients to them

- GPs themselves should integrate complementary therapy into their approach

- Alternative and complementary therapies should be available to medical card holders

- Complementary therapists, osteopaths and sports massage therapists should be fully integrated into the community and hospital care systems

- We must address the culture of over-reliance on prescription medicines.

As well as wanting choice and access, people want complementary medicine and therapy to be properly regulated and the practitioners registered, with standards and accredited training programmes in place. Some called for more research into the effectiveness of complementary medicine.

General practitioner services

There was a lot of interest in the general practitioner services. Proposals focused on the following areas:

- More flexible, 'out-of-hours' services

- More group practices

- Greater access by GPs to diagnostic services

- Concern about the level of GP charges.

People want more GPs, especially in rural areas, but they also want to see new ways of working. These include more group practices, GPs working within local health centres, GPs as part of multi-disciplinary teams, with nursing support as a matter of course and GPs working alongside osteopaths and complementary therapists.

The question of access to a GP at weekends and evenings was raised many times. However, people want to be able to access a GP whom they know and who knows them, at these times.

24-hour access to x-ray and pathology services is needed, according to some contributors. Such extensions in the service and role of the GP would extend the quality of their service, as well as reducing pressure on hospital services.

There were comments about ways in which GPs could improve the quality of their personal interaction with people. Long waiting times in surgeries and very short visits were mentioned, with the GP having little time to talk to people and listen to their concerns. The need for less reliance on prescription medicine was mentioned several times and concern expressed about people's heavy usage of antibiotics. There were concerns too about the perceived unwillingness of GPs to make home visits, especially to older people.

The level of GP charges attracted attention in the submissions and this is reflected in the number of calls for free GP services, especially for children. It was suggested that the high cost of GP services puts pressure on people to go to A&E, or to avoid taking a child to see their doctor when they should. These concerns led to calls for reduced or regulated fees, or for general practitioners on salaries and employed by the health authorities.

There is a detailed proposal for a remuneration package, involving a combination of practice allowance, capitation and service fees. The practice allowance would include a contribution to the running costs of premises, salaries of practice staff and equipment. The capitation payment should reflect the demographic characteristics of the local population. The fee for service could be directed towards public health measures such as immunisation, health promotion and health prevention measures. The contributor believes that this remuneration package could be configured so that it would equal the annual average income of a GP in private practice.

Linkages between services

There was a good deal of concern about poor linkages between services, especially between community services and hospital services. An important concern was the perceived lack of connection between hospitals and GPs, especially when people are being discharged from hospital. The absence of follow-up and the need for better sharing of information came up many times.

Improved information technology is seen as part of the solution to the problem, but also there is a need for more careful discharge planning and pro-active contact among professionals in the hospital and in the community.

People said...

We needed orthodontic treatment for our son, 7 years. There was a waiting list of 6-7 years. So we had to pay £50 per visit, total £300, some visits lasted 2-3 minutes – money for nothing. There is no orthodontic service in -------- Health Board. We need a proper orthodontic service. No-one is worth £50 for 2-3 minutes. **(Male, 40-49, urban)**

Set up GP clinics in each health board area as a trial. Employ GPs to work in these clinics. Charge a reasonable fee or no consultation fee. £25 a consultation is outrageous…a reasonable fee would be £10. **(Male, 40-49, urban)**

GPs who work in groups should have health centres equipped to supply major diagnostic facilities. Such practices should have these facilities supplied and not have to buy such themselves. Should a patient require hospital referral, he/she would arrive with all the necessary investigations already done. **(Male, 60-69, urban)**

District hospitals which were provided in the 19th century and closed during the 20th century should be re-opened to cater for the less serious short-stay acute patient and the long-stay chronic cases. **(Male, 70 plus, urban)**

Locations outside Dublin do not provide even basic support for cancer patients. The establishment of a support group would require minimal funding but would provide huge benefits to the local population. **(Female, 30-39, rural)**

I would like to have a framework in the community which supports keeping people at home instead of seeking beds outside home, the system presently doesn't allow for any reasonable support. Ideas I have would be to start with the very basic needs, courses for carers in how to care and to access services for the elderly. Patients who are incontinent should be covered for special pressure-relieving devices to prevent sores, but also to have a bed bath at least three times a week. In the USA, home-aides provide baths to patients who are incontinent with baths every day when they have a medical condition which is unstable. The cost could be offset by the reduction in admissions by patients who have nobody left to care for them at home because they are exhausted. **(Female, rural)**

My husband had cancer of the prostate and the colon before he died. We had excellent home help, but the nights were very stressful. **(Female, 60-69, rural)**

Chapter 3

Hospital services

Introduction

Proposals for improving hospital services were made in 15 per cent of submissions. The priorities for change were the following:

- The quality and organisation of care

- Waiting lists for elective procedures and out-patient appointments

- The location of services.

The quality and organisation of care

People made a range of proposals about ways of improving the care provided in hospitals, so as to deliver a high quality, user-centred service.

The main focus of attention with regard to organisation was on waiting times for out-patient departments. Other proposals concerned the physical facilities. Inevitably, A&E services and their organisation were raised, though the emphasis was not as great as one might have expected.

Organisational issues and proposals

People are very annoyed by having to wait in out-patient departments. 'Same-time' appointments for large numbers generated strong criticism. There were concerns about losing time from work which for some people means loss of pay. There were concerns too about the long waiting time for people who are ill, people with sick children, pregnant women and older people.

The question of transport arose also in relation to out-patient appointments. If people do not have private transport, the business of lengthy and unpredictable waiting times can cause difficulty.

People feel that out-patient departments should open for much longer periods each day and should work on Saturdays, to facilitate easier access.

While long waiting times persist, people would like to have much better facilities for waiting and more comfortable waiting rooms. The problems for deaf and hard-of-hearing people unable to hear announcements or calls for appointments were raised. Problems of availability and cost of car parking while waiting were also raised.

Other organisational proposals included the following:

- More use of day wards with GP follow-up

- Trauma units in hospitals

- Quicker test results

- Purpose-built units for people with addiction problems.

A&E

Inevitably A&E services were the subject of comment. There were many calls for reduced waiting times and proposals about the way in which A&E services are organised. These included the following:

- Have a GP service in A&E, because many problems should be dealt with at that level

- Lack of out-of-hours GP services and costs putting strain on A&E

- Have a facility in A&E for treating minor injuries

- Have a community-based facility for treating minor injuries

- Ban aggressive drunks – they terrify others, especially older people

- Abolish admissions through A&E

- When a doctor has sent a note for X-ray, one should not have to wait for hours to be seen again by another doctor

- Educate people about the role of A&E

- Levy charges for misuse of A&E

- Have A&E in private hospitals.

Quality of care/service

There were many proposals for improved quality of care and service while in hospital. Some were about medical care while others concerned ways of improving the personal experience of hospital and reducing anxiety or discomfort while in hospital.

There were proposals concerning continuity of consultant cover. People spoke about the need for consultant-led care and continuity of consultant cover. Possibilities mentioned included group consultant practice with 24-hour cover to avoid gaps, and consultant-led services in theatre at all times. The possibility of a senior consultant in the hospital with responsibility for ensuring availability of consultancy services was mentioned also. The availability of epidural services 24-hours a day was raised.

People spoke about the need for reassurance and support when in hospital, especially when one has a condition that is life-threatening. There were proposals, for example, for counsellors for people about to undergo surgery and for people with cancer. There were also suggestions that nursing staff should have more time to spend with people and should engage in more 'hands-on' nursing. There were references to nursing aides as offering a very useful service in supporting people.

People want a more holistic service when in hospital, rather than having each specialty dealing separately with a patient. There were calls for access to complementary medicine while in hospital, sports therapy and massage, as well as trained counsellors, as mentioned already.

Other proposals included:

- More deaf awareness

- Peace and quiet at night

- Less chaotic atmosphere

- Improvements in hygiene in hospitals

- Privacy and personal facilities, such as a place to hang your dressing gown

- Special attention to the needs of older people, e.g. higher chairs, help at mealtimes

- A place where people can die in privacy and dignity, not on wards

- More ward rounds to check on people

- More ward visiting by hospital matrons.

There were many concerns about the poor connections between hospital and community and many calls for better discharge planning, especially for people with strokes who are going home to families who have not been prepared to cope with their needs. Linked to this was concern about people being asked to leave hospital while they felt unfit or unready to leave.

Access to hospital services

Not surprisingly, there were many calls for shorter waiting lists for elective procedures and for treatment of various kinds and reduced waiting times for out-patient appointments.

People often linked these calls to comments about equity and fairness in access to services. Many people see the waiting lists as the result of serious lack of staffing resources and hospital beds. They want to see a big increase in nursing and medical staff, in particular, but also in the other essential staff needed to improve access to services.

The location of services

There were calls for hospital services, including maternity services, to be decentralised and regionalised. Many of these were pleas from people for the establishment or non-closure of hospital facilities in their area, or the opening of facilities that have been built but remain unopened as yet.

The proposals for regional services related to specialisms such as fertility clinics, endocrinology, burns units, medical rehabilitation, ambulance services, neurology services, cancer services, services for pre-term babies and A&E in rural areas.

The 'up-to-Dublin' phenomenon was a concern in many submissions and people felt that it should be possible to avoid the current level of movement of people from rural areas to Dublin and other large centres of population. The inconvenience, the discomfort, cost, time and lack of transport were the main reasons for wanting services delivered more locally.

People said...

I waited 5 months for an appointment to see a rheumatologist. When I eventually got my appointment at [named] Hospital, I took a day's leave. My appointment was at 9.30. At 3.30 that afternoon, I still had not seen Dr. X. and was informed that Dr.X would not be attending his clinic that day. No reason was given and to make matters worse I had to pay £5 in the car park. So I lost a day's leave, was out of pocket for travelling and parking expenses and had a 2-hour journey home. I understand from many people since that this is a common occurrence with Dr. X.'s clinics. I hold a medical card on account of my arthritis. **(Male, 40-49, rural)**

My mother had cellulitis and her doctor had visited her on a few occasions but the antibiotic treatment he had prescribed was not sufficient. He told us to bring her to X Hospital (with a note). She spent all day Sunday 10am-6pm before a doctor attended her. She was admitted and spent from 6pm on Sunday to 6pm on Monday on a trolley before a bed was found. She is 86 years old. **(Male, 50-59, urban)**

Each time I visited the local A&E I received excellent care and attention, I was listened to. Nowadays we senior citizens are treated as fools whose brains are in cold storage, it's frightening to be made to feel worthless. Last visit I had to wait one hour to see the doctor - that did not matter - but the seating in the waiting room was very hard and my poor hips were very painful and sore. When I stood up my lower half was numb. Fortunately there were soft seats in the X-ray waiting room - I now carry a small cushion, one must be prepared and I try to be sensible, we must all do our bit in life. **(Female, over 70, urban)**

It's the weekend, with the usual bed shortages. I feel that a lack of routine tests, for example, x-ray, ultrasounds, CT scans, MRI, angiography, over a weekend period blocks many beds. Many patients who are admitted on Friday have to wait till Monday before any of the above can even be booked. If a patient has any of the above done on Friday they have to wait until Monday for a result if a doctor is not likely to get a verbal report. Has a feasibility study ever been done on having more than a 'skeleton staff' for acute emergencies on our acute hospitals over the weekend? **(Nurse, urban)**

Chapter 4

Health education, health promotion and illness prevention

Introduction

People placed a high priority on health promotion and illness prevention, with more than 1300 proposals on this subject. One can identify some common strands in the wide-ranging material:

- Healthy living is affected by all aspects of people's lives – their nutrition, their environment, lifestyles and income. The supports for healthy living should take account of this 'whole-person, whole society' approach

- People need many different kinds of back-up from the State for healthy living; the help they need crosses the boundaries of state agencies and professional practice – schools, local authorities, various health professionals

- Different age groups and communities need different kinds of support for healthy living.

Health education and health promotion

Health education and health promotion put an onus on individuals to take responsibility for their health and should give them support to do this. The need for a stronger culture of empowerment and personal responsibility for health is highlighted in submissions.

On the subject of positive promotion of healthy living, the submissions concentrated on:

- Ongoing formal health education programmes

- Particular health promotion activities addressed at aspects of lifestyle and health behaviour

- Facilities needed in communities to help people to be healthy and stay healthy.

Formal health education programmes

The proposals place very strong emphasis on the central place of school-based programmes in building the health of the nation, in the long-term. Schools are seen as key sites for health education and health development. Programmes should begin early and extend, in a coherent way, through all the phases and stages of development through to and including third level. The case is made for strong linkages between the Health Strategy and the ongoing work of schools.

As well as wanting formal school-based programmes, the submissions call for high quality sports and gym equipment in schools and facilities which are not weather dependent.

Health promotion activities

In the case of adults, people want greater access to information about all aspects of health, well-being and ways of preventing illness. This information should be broad-ranging, covering areas as diverse as nutrition, the benefits of exercise, car safety for children, food safety, information about the legal age for babysitting, information about high-risk behaviour, objective information about vaccination and information about safe sex.

The way in which information is provided is discussed in the submissions. People are sceptical about leaflets and more enthusiastic about television as a good medium for health education.

People who are disadvantaged should get practical support for healthy living and not just information. The State should provide subsidy for healthy food, support for people with literacy problems, and adequate income. There was a suggestion that the post of 'health visitor' should be set up, who would give people practical advice about healthy living.

One key point made in the submissions is that all health professionals should see themselves as having a role in health education and health promotion. GPs should give information about nutrition; they should refer people to exercise programmes, the emphasis should be taken off medication and a more holistic approach to health should be adopted. It was suggested that this is especially important for children, who should learn from an early age to avoid over-reliance on medication.

Several contributors draw attention to the need for support for breastfeeding, as an aspect of health promotion. More advice and guidance, more access to mothers who have breastfed successfully and longer periods of maternity leave are among the proposals on this topic.

While much of the material concentrates on physical fitness, there is concern too about the need to promote and develop positive mental health. Access to stress management courses and yoga is mentioned. There should be a named person on school staffs, according to one submission, who would 'look out for' young people's mental health and development and draw attention to any early signs of problems. An end to 'high stakes' academic testing of children and young people was proposed.

Facilities for healthy living

The submissions envisage several kinds of facilities in the community to help promote and support healthy living. Some of these would be the responsibility of the health services, others need to be provided by local authorities and private providers.

Community-based 'healthy living centres' are needed, according to submissions. There is favourable mention of such a centre in Kilkenny. Telephone helplines and healthy living advice services should be provided, staffed by health professionals.

There were many calls for free or subsidised gyms and leisure centres. Contributors point out that, at the moment, only better-off people can go to a gym or leisure centre. Better play areas, swimming pools and parks are needed; these should be included in area and community planning. There should be an onus on builders to provide leisure facilities when building housing estates.

The proposal is also made that school facilities should be available to local communities outside school hours. The need for more time for breaks and for eating lunch in school is raised in one lengthy submission, which argues that present arrangements have long-term negative effects on children's eating habits and their health.

Illness prevention

The proposals on illness prevention fell into two main groups:

- State action needed to reduce or stop unhealthy lifestyles or health threatening activities

- Screening facilities to identify potential health risks.

Prevention

The main prevention initiatives concern smoking. There are also proposals to address alcohol abuse, drug abuse and gambling addiction. There were a small number of proposals about dealing with obesity as a growing health problem. The prevention initiatives proposed to help reduce smoking included the following:

- Place a complete ban on smoking

- Ban smoking in any public place

- Ban all advertising

- Prevent sporting organisations from accepting sponsorship from cigarette manufacturers

- Tax profits on tobacco products more heavily

- Charge £5 for packet of 20 cigarettes

- Make it possible for people to recoup the costs of smoking-related illness from cigarette manufacturers

- Ban cigarette machines.

Proposals concerning alcohol abuse include the banning of alcohol at discos and a lifetime ban from driving for a conviction for drunken driving.

Other prevention proposals were:

- Introduce tighter controls on food quality and higher fines for breaches of food safety legislation

- More inspections in workplaces by health and safety inspectorate

- Give people a choice about fluoridation

- Enforce seat-belt laws

- Address the weight of schoolbags

- Shut Sellafield.

Health screening

There were calls for access to systematic local health screening for everyone, as well as proposals for particular checks for men's health, women's health, children's health and development. Many people proposed that these checks should be free. The main proposals were the following:

- Access to an annual health check, free of charge, e.g. for blood pressure, cholesterol levels

- Access in all parts of the country to breast check and cervical check; access to breast screening for women of all ages

- Men's health checks, in particular checks for prostate and testicular cancer

- Developmental checks for all children under 5 years.

People said...

We need changes in our lifestyles so the best way to promote health is to start young. 'The baby at one is the man at forty' once quoted by a doctor and this is very true. Let's start young and instill in children the importance of health. **(Female, 40-49, rural)**

A lack of community centres on housing estates i.e lack of social facilities to develop a community spirit is a contributory factor [to alcohol abuse]. Non-provision of a civilised alternative by local/central government. **(Anon)**

Vested interests in the tobacco, drinks, fast food and proprietary drugs empires will successfully defeat all the best intentions of the Minister for Health. The high cost of medicine and treatment and the 'specialist' syndrome will effectively swallow the health budget. **(Female, urban)**

Hypnotherapy, replacement therapy should all be available free of charge for those who want to quit smoking. **(Female, 20-29, urban)**

Lots of people are couch potatoes, smoke lots, drink to excess often, eat poor quality fatty foods, then want medicine to cure their ills….Schools locked up at 3.30 pm and all during weekends, holidays could be used for sports, dance, yoga, tai chi, meditation. All these could be taught very easily and would benefit people hugely….Very few doctors ask people about diet, exercise etc. Support workers and paramedics could be trained as educators to assist doctors….meeting in peer groups in own area with good facilitators for 4-5 weekly sessions to promote exercise, healthy eating, etc. **(Male, 50-59, urban)**

Incentives to take up lifelong learning opportunities as a way to encourage mental and physical activity throughout life and reduce dependence on TV, drink, food as major leisure activities. **(Female, 30-39, rural)**

Health education – the public needs to take care of itself. They need to understand that they are solely responsible for their own health as to their diet, smoking etc. Their environment – air, water (unfluoridated) and pollution-free food should be the responsibility of the Government. **(Female, 40-49, rural)**

The greatest benefit for the greatest number of people is the immediate shut-down of Sellafield nuclear facility – a public health disaster waiting to happen. Prevention now. **(Female, 50-59, rural)**

Tax relief incentives for both consumers and providers could be aimed at lifestyle choices for health (sport, organic food, cycling) and non-therapeutic healthcare (vitamins, seaweed baths, chiropractic, gym membership, massage), much like when we needed industry and investment the government provided tax relief incentives for this. Could this be done with the country's urgent need for health?

[We need] help and counselling for people with overambitious and tense lives. Relaxation classes taught in hospitals, health centres, secondary schools. Co-operation and community values should be encouraged to get people to help each other. **(Female, 40-49, urban)**

I suggest that the Department move the breastfeeding policy up on the health promotion agenda. The benefits of breastfeeding in preventing illness in both mother and baby have been widely researched. **(Female, 30-39, urban)**

Chapter 5

Equality, equity, entitlements

Introduction

Just over 10 per cent of proposals were concerned with issues of equality and the linked issue of entitlements.

People want fair access to health services, based on need, not on personal resources. People called for an end to what was widely referred to as a 'two-tier' system. There were some views as to the way in which a fair system would be financed, with calls for both an entirely tax-based system and an insurance-based system. There were some calls for an end to consultant access to private facilities in public hospitals and for private A&E facilities.

Many contributors suggested that we implement systems like those in use in other countries. France and Britain were mentioned most often, but also Denmark, Canada and Australia.

Much of the discussion focused in on the question of individual entitlements, in particular the medical card system and the arrangements for meeting people's health costs.

Medical cards

Among those who made proposals for changes to the medical card arrangements, the main changes proposed were:

• Medical card/free GP services for children and young people

• Extension of the medical card to extra groups

• Change in the income limits which govern the medical card.

There were also proposals for improvements in the range of services available to medical card holders including freedom to choose their own doctor.

It was felt that money should never stop people from bringing a child to see a doctor and that the cost of GP visits stops people at present, especially when a child is ill regularly, or when there are several children in a family.

The views about extending free health services to children and young people ranged from providing free healthcare to children under 5 to providing medical cards for all school children or to everyone in formal education, including apprenticeships.

Several additional groups should get medical cards, according to submissions. These include people entitled to the Long-Term Illness Scheme, people with chronic conditions, people with disabilities, lone parents and small farmers with no off-farm income.

The medical card should cover complementary medicine, counselling and fertility treatment.

Private healthcare

Many people questioned the equity of the system through which people pay tax and PRSI and must then buy health insurance to pay for health services.

Some older people argued that, having worked all their lives and paid taxes, they have already paid for health services and should not have to pay twice, for example, for nursing home care.

Several people made proposals for changes in insurance cover for those who are members of private insurance schemes. Fertility treatment was mentioned and treatment for those with gender dysphoria (GID). Cover for people with Alzheimer's disease was also proposed. It should be possible to claim back the total cost of doctor's fees, according to a number of submissions.

For those who do not have a medical card, there were many proposals that GP fees should be regulated or reduced. There were some suggestions that consultants' fees should be published so that people can choose the lowest price.

Universal free services

Even within the current arrangements where there is a 'mix' of public and private medical care, people feel that some health services should be free to everyone. As noted already, many people feel that all children's health needs should be met without charge.

There were proposals for free health screening for all. Free access to contraception was also suggested.

Other proposals

The Drugs Payment Scheme was raised by some contributors, who feel that prescription medicines are too expensive and that cheap, effective drugs should be available to everyone. There was a view that the £42 per month charge is too high. Free prescription medicine for all children was suggested.

People said...

I must keep up private health insurance to be certain of obtaining treatment within a reasonable time and it appears this must continue for the remainder of my life and that of my wife.

This is not a complaint, but is a statement of the situation for all staff employees of many state/semi-state employees and employees that are broadly aligned with state conditions. We are in a kind of limbo situation regarding many state services, including health. **(Male, 60-69, urban)**

I feel very strongly about the fact that GPs should be free for children or at least prescription medicine. On a personal level I spent over £380 on GP visits last year for my family. I can't even begin to add up what was purchased in the chemist. I believe if people could see their GP every time they were sick [instead of putting it off because they can't afford it] then the whole population would be a lot healthier at the end of the day. **(Female, 30-39, urban)**

A private health service should become a memory if plans for a decent public health service become a reality. I have doubts if this will ever happen in Ireland because of vested interests. **(Male, 50-59, urban)**

No parent should have to question whether or not their child's illness warrants an outlay of £25. **(Female, 30-39, rural)**

There is a shocking division in this country between the richer, better educated people who can afford decent healthcare and those who cannot. The latter group is struggling with a lack of information about health as well as a basic inability to afford it. If money is not ploughed into the system now the vision of Ireland's future is a terrifying one. **(Female, 30-39, rural)**

Where one is provided with a companion travel pass would it be possible to provide a voucher for the return journey to the companion where the holder of the pass is admitted to hospital and is not returning?

Special tax exemptions are given to people caring for relatives over 70. Why are these exemptions not given to the aged person where such a person is managing on their own, by paying odd job people etc or just going without needed care? Not everybody has willing relatives or in fact any. **(Female, 70 plus, rural)**

Regulate VHI – make it easy for the insured to get their claims met. It should be possible to do it all in real time with IT links between doctors, hospitals, specialist, pharmacies and the VHI. **(Male, 50-59, urban)**

Change the medical scheme of £42 per month to include something towards doctors' fees. Often tablets can cost as little as £5 but doctors' fees £25/30. **(Male, 40-49, urban)**

Deireadh a chur leis an táille £42 míosula, ar taibléidí is ar uile, is mór an méid é seo nuair atá tú ar phinsin beag. **(Male, 60-69, urban)**

Private doctors' fees are way too high. A lot of women who don't work and don't have a medical card don't look after themselves because they can't afford to go to the doctor. **(Female, 50-59, urban)**

Having left full time employment to care for my wife four and a half years ago and now am a full time carer in the home, the State allows me £3 more than dole for this. I have voiced this as a disgrace with ministers. It does not seem we are worth more. Caring is done out of love. A little extra money would help to pay bills. **(Male, 50-59, urban)**

The total cost of my stay at the [named] nursing home was about £5,000. I had to borrow some of this from a friend of mine and try to pay it from my old age pension... **(Male, over 70, rural)**

Chapter 6

Quality and accountability systems

Introduction

In 7 per cent of the proposals, people discussed the need for systems to monitor and enhance quality, effectiveness, efficiency and accountability in health services.

Increased levels of staffing of all kinds are needed in the health system, as well as improved investment in staff training at all levels. These developments are seen as crucial to improving quality of service. Shortages in all grades of staff are mentioned, but in particular the shortages of doctors and nurses. Changes to entry systems for both nurses and doctors are proposed.

There is quite a lot of ongoing concern about the hours worked by junior doctors and concern that trainee doctors should be fully supervised.

Among the many quality and accountability system proposals were the following:

- Mandatory reporting of adverse incidents in hospitals

- Legislation to make Medical Council hearings more transparent and accessible

- A league table for hospitals

- Annual reviews and comparisons between health boards

- Audits of health board spending

- Benchmarking of different hospital departments

- Case managers, who would adopt a 'whole-person' approach to care for each individual

- Elimination of waste in hospitals and health services

- Spot-checks on A&E in rural areas

- Review of the practices of doctors and consultants with regard to charges, appointment systems, standards of care

- Lower ratios of administrative staff

- Independent monitoring of professionals

- Strict enforcement of state registration systems.

People said...

My earnest plea from the heart is for a campaign to address and eliminate hospital mistakes. One mistake and one near miss is one too many, believe me. We have a road safety campaign and quite rightly so, we now need a hospital safety campaign. **(Female, 50-59, urban)**

Cut out the layers of management in the health board and at hospital level and have staff members more accountable for the jobs they do – being sent around from one to another in search of information is time-wasting, frustrating and leads to anger. **(Female, 40-49, rural)**

If more money is given to hospitals, I would like it done in such a way that a better, not just a better funded service is delivered to the public. This could mean patient evaluation of hospital treatment, continual surveys of patient cases, funding being delivered in proportion to how efficiently they are being run and how well services are being delivered to their patients … **(Male, 30-39, urban)**

(I propose) the Minister forms a new Inspectorate on a multidisciplinary basis, to oversee the delivery of services in all areas of health board services. **(Female, 40-49, rural)**

Chapter 7

People's experiences of the health services

Introduction

In this chapter, the feedback about people's experiences of the health services is described. The main source of comment about people's experiences come from the responses to Question 1 in the consultation pack *Your Views About Health*, in which people were asked to describe positive, negative or mixed experiences and to talk about why they rated their experience as positive, negative or mixed.

Material on this topic was also contained in the views given in response to the invitation in the consultation pack to suggest ways of enhancing people's health and well-being.

In 7.1 below, an account is given of the kinds of positive and negative experiences described in a sample of submissions. In 7.2, the proposals people made for improving people's experience of the health services are outlined.

7.1 **Positive, negative and mixed experiences of health services**

Question 1 contained both a quantitative and a qualitative element and was posed as follows:

1. **Have your recent experiences of health services been good or bad or mixed?**
   (Please tick Box)

   Good ❑   Bad ❑   Mixed ❑

   Can you tell us more about what made your experiences good or bad?

The responses to this question generated qualitative material that provides an in-depth insight into people's personal experiences of the health services.

The range of aspects of the health services addressed in the responses was very broad. Most people seem to have devoted a good deal of attention to this question and have written at some length on it. Some have devoted their attention entirely to one aspect of the health services while others have mentioned up to ten.

There is a level of emotion and depth of human feeling in the responses which might not necessarily have been expected, given the relatively impersonal nature of the exercise. Also, it is very clear that people were most anxious to be as fair as they could to the health services and were anxious to draw out positive as well as negative aspects.

Extracts from the material are included to exemplify the range of areas and perceptions which emerged as being of most significance. This will be matched by a more quantitative analysis which gives an overview of the numbers mentioning the various aspects of the health services.

Responses to Question 1, Part 1
Have your recent experiences of the health services been good or bad or mixed?

More than 90 per cent (1359) of the 1512 respondents replied to the invitation to describe their experiences of the health services. Of these, the majority (52 per cent) said their experiences had been mixed. Almost one-fifth (19 per cent) described positive experiences, while a slightly higher number (21 per cent) said their experiences had been negative.

Responses to Question 1, Part 2
Can you tell us more about what made your experiences good or bad?

The thousands of good and bad experiences that have been described provide an important insight into the day-to-day experience of the public in their involvement with the health services. The good experiences described point to examples of best practice in health services that can be built upon in the future. The negative experiences can be examined by policy makers, staff and management of the health services, to see what guidance they offer for enhancing service delivery 'on the ground'.

For the purpose of this report, a flavour of the experiences described is given, drawing on a sample of 300 (20 per cent) of the submissions. On account of the importance of this material, the Department of Health and Children has decided that a separate analysis of this material should be prepared. This work will be completed in the coming months.

The findings

Responses were grouped according to the area or aspect of the health service about which people wrote, for example, acute hospital services, general practitioner service, community care services.

The number of mentions, both positive and negative, which were made about the various aspects of the health services in the sample are presented in Table 2.

Table 2: **Aspects of the health services mentioned in sample of responses to Question 1 (presented in rank order and including breakdown by positive and negative mentions):**

	No. of Mentions		
Aspect	Positive	Negative	Total (N=300)
Acute In-Patient	58 (45%)	70 (55%)	128 (100%)
A+E	9 (17%)	46 (83%)	55 (100%)
Community Care	22 (44%)	30 (56%)	52 (100%)
Out-patients Clinics	12 (25%)	37 (75%)	49 (100%)
Disability/LTI	11 (33%)	23 (67%)	34 (100%)
GP Services	17 (57%)	13 (43%)	30 (100%)
Maternity Services	9 (39%)	14 (61%)	23 (100%)
Services for Older People	4 (24%)	13 (76%)	17 (100%)

The key points arising from Table 2 can be summarised as follows:

• Acute in-patient services were mentioned more than other aspects

• GP services received the highest percentage (57 per cent) of positive mentions

• Accident and emergency received the highest percentage (83 per cent) of negative mentions.

While accident and emergency received a total of only 17 per cent of positive mentions, the corresponding percentage for acute in-patient care was 45 per cent, suggesting that when people get into hospital, they are relatively satisfied with the care received. This point was discussed in a number of the submissions. One woman in the Dublin area commented on this as follows:

> The unfortunate situation is in casualty, but it's only because of the shortage of doctors and nurses. It's such a pity because the attention a patient gets when they get into hospital is really excellent. Hopefully, this unfortunate situation will be sorted.

Acute in-patient services

Those who made positive comments about acute in-patient experiences tended to focus very much on medical and nursing care. In most cases, the positive comments came from people who stated that they either had private health insurance cover or were themselves healthcare workers. However, there were a few exceptions to this as the following extract from a woman over seventy years of age exemplifies:

> As a medical card patient...I had a thyroid operation 5 years ago. I was called for same within 5 weeks of being diagnosed. The surgeon and all the staff were excellent. More recently, I was in the same hospital for arm and chest pain and I have the highest praise for all the staff.

Those who focused on the experience of children in hospital were equally divided between positive and negative comments. One of the parents who experienced good treatment for their child and good facilities for parents wrote as follows:

> My son was admitted to hospital in 2000. He is 5-years-old and had had previous bad experiences with doctors and needles etc. This was explained to the paediatric staff who were most obliging in helping my son to overcome his fears. The new paediatric wing in ... is very, very family orientated and I was able to stay, in considerable comfort, with my son which was most beneficial to us both. I think the new awareness to a child's response to healthcare was long overdue but gladly welcomed.

On the negative side, there tended to be far longer comments and many more aspects of the negative experience described. The main issues, which arose here, were:

• Poor facilities

• Staff shortages

• Inadequate provision for terminally ill patients

• Early discharge

• Difficulties around making complaints

• Inadequate provision for people in general hospitals for people with communication difficulties - e.g. people with Alzheimer's disease, autism

• Poor attitudes towards elderly people.

The following are by no means the most extreme examples but give a good indication of the sorts of experiences which people described:

> I spent 7 days in what was supposed to be a semi-private room. There was no head light, the back support was broken. The quilt on the bed had about 20 holes in it, like as if a mouse had eaten it. The food was by no means good. There was no privacy. When the consultant did his rounds he shouted out your complaints. I knew what was going to happen to the person in the next bed. There was no person to make a complaint to, as the Matron did not do any rounds.

Another person wrote of his experience of having coronary by-pass surgery:

> Told I'd be 48 hours in ICU - out in less than less than 24 hours - due to **bed pressure**; told 48 hours in observation ward - out in less than 12 hours due to **bed pressure**. Told not being discharged until **weekend** - out on Wed. Asked to go - 'they need the bed' - left ward accompanied by my wife and son and walked to lifts and then front door accompanied by staff- very weak - but successful bed appropriation. Staff totally overworked in pressure to relieve waiting lists; all patients seriously ill but no increase in nursing staff whose workload is doubled by not having any recovering patients. Discharged with septic leg wound. VHI patients treated equally to public patients - all equal in a war zone - not a health facility.

An 80-year-old man wrote at length of his experience of a general hospital where he was admitted with double pneumonia. For him, one of the worst aspects related to the way he was treated at the hospital:

> I asked for a urine bottle and the Sister in Charge told me to wait. I told her I would have to do it on the floor. She replied, 'Do it away'…Would you please teach them kindness and good manners to all their patients and to all old folk.

There are 17 mentions of consultant services. This is perhaps the area where strong feelings are discernible among those who made negative comments. 2 of the 4 who made positive comments summed up their views with words like 'excellent' and 'thorough'.

The 13 negative comments were focused mainly on attitudes to patients. The following extract highlights the experience of someone who describes the impact of dealing with differing attitudes:

> While my mother-in-law's consultant was extremely helpful and made an appointment to see the family in his office to give us more details and answer any queries we had in relation to the disease and life expectancy etc, we found the exact opposite in my mother's consultant. I was informed of the diagnosis on my own at the bottom of the ward by one of his team. It was very hard to get an appointment with the consultant and even then he insisted on speaking to one member of the family only. We found all this very distressing and the lack of information made it seem worse.

Accident and emergency

As we have seen, accident and emergency departments emerged as being problematical with 83 per cent of the mentions being negative. Also, A&E ranked second in terms of the actual number (55) of mentions made in this sample.

In the 9 positive mentions, the point made was that the care and treatment which had been received were good. Most of these also made reference to waiting times - saying either that they had had to wait for hours before the good treatment/care or had been lucky in terms of when they had actually arrived. The extract below is typical of this latter type of case:

> …the hospital was fairly quiet and my son received prompt and good treatment for a hand injury. We were lucky to arrive at the right time of a Saturday night. The advertised waiting time according to a sign in the hospital is 8 hours - unacceptably long for the ill, for workers and the elderly.

On the negative side, 3 key themes arose regularly. These were long waiting times, poor communication and poor facilities.

The following extracts highlight the kinds of experiences reported:

> My mother, who is 84, was left in A&E for 24 hours without anything to eat. In that period she got one cup of tea and a slice of bread. She had been brought to the hospital by ambulance at 4pm and when I arrived at about 7pm she was in the corridor on a trolley. I asked for a cup of tea for her. However, she got a cup of water; it was not until the following day that she was given the tea and bread. That was her total intake of food in 24 hours. Also, when I rang later in the evening to enquire re her condition. She had a dislocated shoulder. I asked the doctor what was the procedure for her shoulder. I was told and I quote, 'Do you want a step by step description of what is to be done?'

Another account from a person over seventy years of age reads as follows:

> Live alone and got ill on a Friday night at midnight. Could not get a GP. Taken to hospital; taxi cost £20. Patients and stretchers in A&E. Had tests and x-rays. Put in a small room in A&E. Two other patients there. One very ill - died since from cancer. The other an 18 year old, watching TV. Time 2.45am. Had a few calls on her mobile. Said she had ME. Ten teenagers arrived Saturday morning with mobiles. Noise was unbelievable. Order chicken and chips from a take-away machine. Imagine the smell in the room and the dear lady with cancer. I sat in Casualty all day Sunday; Monday was similar. Tuesday I told the doctor and he moved us. Over the next 10 days I was in 6 different beds. Nurses trying to make room.

Community care

With regard to community care services, the percentage of positive comments (44 per cent) is less than the percentage of negative observations (56 per cent). The number of mentions in the sample (52) was relatively low, given the range of services that are within this particular area.

The aspects of the community care services which received attention were wide ranging and it is difficult to draw out any definite trends as the same person could have had mixed experiences in relation to the same service.

A service which emerged with much praise, was the ambulance service. Although numbers of comments were low, there were no negative comments and people expressed great appreciation for the speed and helpfulness of the ambulance crews.

HEALTH SCIENCES BROOKFIELD LIBRARY CORK

On the negative side, the aspects covered were also quite diverse but there were more negative comments about domiciliary care for elderly people than other aspects. The following extract was typical in this regard:

> *Caring for elderly mother five years ago, it was impossible to get relief services. Home help was not always available and nursing help was not always regular. I felt she could have stayed out of nursing home if more help was available.*

Other problematical areas, which were identified, included lack of counselling, lack of physiotherapy services, lack of availability of smear testing and dental services for children.

Out-patient clinics

As with A&E, the submissions revealed that out-patient clinics are a cause for concern among the public. They rated fourth in terms of number of mentions in the sample of 300 submissions (49) and 75 per cent of those were negative.

Of the 25 per cent who made positive comments, there was strong satisfaction with the skill and professionalism of the staff involved. The following extract is very typical of these:

> *One of my sons was treated by out-patient specialist clinic. I felt at all times that his individuality, dignity and minor worries were given the required importance.*

The main areas of dissatisfaction centred on long waiting periods for appointments, long waiting times at clinics, poor communication skills and attitudes among staff, poor facilities and over reliance on senior house officers.

On waiting for appointments at clinics, the following extract from a woman in her forties is typical:

> *My GP sent a letter requesting a radiological procedure on my behalf to the hospital in Dec 2000. I am still waiting for an appointment. Each time I phone about my appointment I am told that, 'I'm in the system', but they could not tell me when I will get an appointment. I was told it depended on the Consultant who 'revises the requests weekly'. I may never be called.*

The dissatisfaction of one woman in her fifties concerning the clinic relevant to her was expressed as follows:

> *The Clinic at the hospital is like a centre for a herd of cattle. No privacy. Nurses station in the middle of an open area. Kept hours waiting for an appointment. No dignity of person.*

Disability and long-term illness

The percentage of negative (67 per cent) comments outweighed the positive (33 per cent) in relation to the references to services for people with disabilities and long-term illnesses. On the positive side, the main emphasis was on the strengths of particular centres for people with disabilities. Also, there were positive comments on services relating to some specific illnesses such as diabetes.

On the negative side, the comments almost all centred on the lack of provision of services for people with mental health problems and Alzheimer's disease. Poor provision for people with deafness, ME and dyspraxia were also mentioned.

Most of the negative comments about mental health were focused on depression and the following extract was typical of these:

> My mother suffers from depression and has done all her life. She is 66 now. I am 29 and live with my parents. I have witnessed my mother being admitted to hospital after hospital for depression and have seen how very little help there is ... I am appalled at the lack of help out there for sufferers of depression. She goes to a clinic each week, only to receive her medication. There seems to be no time available to chat to people, to find out how they are, how things are going for them etc. They are rushed in and out, like luggage on a conveyor belt... Families have to go through hell with their depressed loved ones, not being able to help them enough themselves. We can only do so much, but something more is needed.

The point that there is little support available for the families of people with depression was made in a number of other submissions, which concurred with the views set out in the extract above.

On the subject of provision for people with Alzheimer's disease, this extract from a woman in her thirties draws together most of the key points made:

> Alzheimer's patients get very poor care. My father could not get any hospital care. My mother was told she could not get a home help as nobody would be able to handle him. Eventually, he needed full-time hospital care. No hospital/health service nursing home would take him. There were beds available but he was not eligible for them as he had a private pension. After much searching we eventually got him into a private nursing home, costing approx. £16,000 p/a which we got no government support for. Also, although he paid into VHI all his life he was not entitled to a penny here also. There seems to be no care for the elderly.

General practitioner services

General practitioner services received a high 'satisfaction' rating with 57 per cent of the comments being positive. On the negative side, the cost of GP services was the most dominant theme, with reluctance to make domiciliary visits rating second and perceived inadequacies in terms of support for mental health problems and openness to alternative medicine being mentioned in a couple of cases. On the cost issue, the main area of concern related to the cost involved in bringing children to the GP. The following extract is typical in this regard:

> Having two young children - aged 7 months and 3 years, I have attended the local GP approximately 10 times (excluding vaccination visits) over the last 3 months. At £20 plus a visit, this is very costly. I think every child under 5 years of age should be entitled to a medical card. With pressures of modern life and two parents in most families working, children are in contact with others socially at a much younger age, crèche, playgroups, pre-school, hence when one child gets sick everyone else picks up the 'bug'.

Maternity services

Comments relating to the whole maternity process were categorised under this heading i.e. antenatal, birth experience/s, including maternity hospital care and postnatal care. The number of comments was relatively low at just 23 and of these 39 per cent were positive and 61 per cent were negative.

The positive comments centred mainly on hospital experiences and postnatal care. The following extracts exemplify the points raised:

I had a baby recently (7 months ago). Both the services and supports (doctor and classes for antenatal) and the hospital and public health nurses were excellent. The hospital was brilliant when I had my second child delivered there. The midwives were absolutely brilliant, very helpful and most importantly, very informative.

The negative comments touched on quite a wide range of issues but particular emphasis was placed on poor communication and information especially about breastfeeding, staff shortages, poor facilities, poor staff attitudes and cost issues.

A woman in her 30s, who was 4 months pregnant, wrote about poor facilities in a manner typical of a number of others:

No privacy when giving blood, urine testing and taking blood pressure - an average of 4 women ahead of you and 4 women behind you. All comments by nursing staff can be heard by all, including comments on previous still births, miscarriages and STDs. Heavily-pregnant women expected to sit on stairs while awaiting a meeting with the doctor.

Services for older people

The number of comments (17) on community services for older people was relatively low. The balance, here again, was very much toward negative comments (76 per cent).

The 4 positive comments related to particular day care centres (2), a short-term nursing home experience and community care services at home. The main focus of the negative comments was on a lack of domiciliary care services, problems with aftercare following hospital stays and attitudes to older people.

On negative attitudes to older people, the following, from a woman in her 40s with an elderly relative, is typical:

The elderly are treated as though they should be grateful for any treatment given to them even when this undermines their dignity and privacy. At times, the elderly are treated like children or as though they are intellectually impaired. For example, treatment, tests, results, diagnoses etc are not given to them so that they are in a state of fear as to what is actually wrong with them and what will happen them. In my experience, only some health professionals will actually talk to the elderly.

Hospice

The hospice service received 4 mentions in the 300 submissions reviewed. All mentions were positive. One woman who had experience of the terminal care of relatives in both a general hospital and a hospice wrote as follows:

Two members of my family died in the same hospital in the last few years. They were left in the ward with other people. Not shown much respect for people dying. My mother died 3 years ago in a hospice and there was a big difference in care. No matter where people die, they deserve to be treated with respect and given comfort and let them die with dignity. This should be the policy of hospitals.

7.2 **Improving people's experience of health services**

About 5 per cent of the proposals contained in submissions concerned ways in which people's experience of dealing with health services and health service personnel could be improved. Although not a large percentage, by comparison with the number of proposals on matters such as community health services and hospital services, people nonetheless raised important issues that are linked to the objective of developing a people-centred health service.

The main proposals as to ways of improving people's experience of contact with health services fell under the following headings:

- More openness and involvement in matters to do with one's own health

- More information about entitlements

- Courtesy, respect and listening

- Training for staff in customer care/relations

- Complaints and appeals procedures

- Consultation

- User-friendly procedures.

Openness and involvement in one's own healthcare

People want to play an active part in matters to do with their own health issues or health treatment. They want to be given information, in simple language, to be told about options and to make their own choices. The point is made that people are often afraid to ask questions and that there exists something of a culture of reticence. There is a 'controlling mindset' among some professionals, according to one contributor who argues that this ethos needs to change.

People would like to be told how long they must wait to see a consultant or have a procedure done and for that information to be updated from time to time. They would like to know what to expect after surgery and they would like to know how best to help themselves and aid recovery after treatment.

Information

People want much more access to general information about their entitlements. This should not just be through provision of leaflets. They would like to be able to talk to personnel who can answer questions. Health information centres or information staff in health centres are proposed. People want to be able to access information about health-related social welfare benefits such as optical and dental benefits in such health information services.

Information services should be accessible outside standard working hours and should take account of the special needs of people from different cultural backgrounds. Directories of services for each health board area would be useful.

Positive attitudes, listening and respect

The general thrust of comments on this topic concerned the need for training for all health service personnel in communicating with people who use health services; training in explaining issues and problems, training in expressing regret when things go wrong, understanding people's vulnerability and talking to people who have lost a relative through suicide.

There was special mention of older people, people with mental health difficulties, parents and people who are deaf as needing particular levels of empathy and understanding.

The terms respect, dignity and courtesy come up a number of times; there was concern at what some people have experienced as arrogance and discourtesy.

Some of the comments made about these matters included the following:

- Take admission notes in private

- Don't talk about people in front of others

- Have manners with sick and old people

- Do not discuss people with junior doctors as if they were objects

- Take tests in private

- Don't postpone appointments at short notice.

Complaints procedures

There are several calls for the establishment of a Health Ombudsman's Office, as well as complaints procedures for all kinds of services and institutions. Patient advocacy services are proposed too. The need for complaints procedures is linked to the need for rights for patients and service users.

Consultation

The proposals about consultation include both permanent consultation processes, such as community health councils, as well as once-off satisfaction checks with users of services.

Consumers and carers should be directly represented on all health board committees; there should be more open forums for debate on health services.

User-friendly procedures

Many people called for user-friendly procedures, which can be handled well by everyone, including people from different cultural and language backgrounds. People are looking for less bureaucracy and paperwork. The need for sensitive assessment systems is mentioned, for example in relation to supplementary welfare benefit. Improvements in adoption assessment procedures are also proposed.

People said ...

[We recommend] the appointment of an Ombudsman for health services. Most of the complaints about the health services discussed in social settings are valid and we the public are unsure as to whom we should address our complaints. We are very vulnerable when we are ill and we all (public and private patients) deserve a truly caring, respectful healthcare system and an Ombudsman to ensure that we get what we need when we need it.
We would like to be able to give our views on an ongoing basis. **(Family, rural)**

While living in [health board] area, I experienced excellent attention from health board personnel and I found that much improvement was made in the last few years to make services more accessible to people and families when needed. **(Female, 50-59, rural)**

*The new health centre is a big improvement on old one – TV in waiting room and a water dispenser...***(Female, 30-39)**

*Our son has cerebral palsy. He is 3-years old. We have had nothing but a hard time from the health board in those 3 years...I could write a book on this but at the moment I am too annoyed to write...***(Parents, 30-39, rural)**

In a patient-focused service, patients would be viewed as the primary stakeholder. Health Strategy 2001 does not appear to have any patient representative on the Steering Group nor the Project Team. This Consultation Form is an effort, but a very weak one. And rather condescending in trying to gain an 'understanding of the difficulties ordinary people face' with the current health service. A serious effort in this regard would seek to establish a major Group/Team representing patients. Breakthroughs in the quality of health service care will not come by simply nudging the sectoral interests of the current service providers who constitute the current system. **(Family, rural)**

My son is on Category 2 waiting list [for dental care] since October 1996...I phone every year to see what's happening. No-one ever phones me! **(Female, 40-49, urban)**

Strategies and Charters are all very well but if they don't reach the bedside they are less than useless. The Patient's Charter was foolish in that regard. What must be done is to take one hospital or one area – interview all staff - discuss the seriousness of healthcare and how much each one is prepared to apply the personal consequences to making that hospital/area a truly health restoring place. **(Female, 60-69, rural)**

And finally...

The birth of my son in [named regional hospital]. The whole staff were spectacular.
Undoubtedly the most moving experience of people who do so much more than a job,
that it actually began to restore my faith in a fast falling society. **(Male, 40-45, rural).**

PART 2

Views and proposals from organisations

Introduction   51

Chapter 1: Health promotion and illness prevention   53

Chapter 2: Acute care and maternity services   56

Chapter 3: Funding, equity, eligibility and entitlements   62

Chapter 4: Quality in health services   67

Chapter 5: Human resources   72

Chapter 6: Community-based health and personal social services   77

Chapter 7: Meeting the needs of older people   87

Chapter 8: Meeting the needs of people with disabilities   93

Chapter 9: The infrastructure of the health system   104

Chapter 10: People's experiences of the health services   111

Introduction

Consulting organisations

The consultation process

A wide range of national and local organisations responded to the invitation to make written submissions. Many national organisations participated directly in the work of preparing the Health Strategy, through their involvement in the National Health Strategy Consultative Forum and several of these also made written submissions. This report describes the feedback contained in the submissions from organisations.

The analysis of submissions

All submissions were coded using the framework developed for the analysis of submissions from members of the public, with some minor adjustments. The proposals in each submission were entered onto a database. The material was then drawn together, under each of the headings of the framework and a report on the main findings prepared.

The respondents

Submissions were received from over 300 organisations, in the following categories:

- National federations and representative bodies working in the Voluntary and Community Sector

- Service providers in the Voluntary and Community Sector

- National advocacy and support organisations

- Local advocacy and support groups

- Private sector health service providers

- Trade unions

- Organisations and groups of health professionals

- Government agencies

- Local authorities

- Academic groups

- Representative bodies of private providers.

A list of organisations who made submissions is given in Appendix 3.

Reporting on the consultation findings

As noted already, reports on the outcomes of the consultation process were provided to the various groups working on the preparation of the Strategy. The findings were also outlined at the National Health Strategy Consultative Forum Conference in July, 2001.

This report gives an overview of the views and proposals on each of the main themes discussed in the submissions. Commonly held views are summarised. A range of the particular concerns raised by individual organisations is also described. Extracts from submissions are used from time to time to exemplify points.

The analysis and report are thematic, rather than quantitative. There are a number of reasons for this approach:

- Not all respondents addressed all issues

- The length and complexity of the responses varied considerably, from a few pages to over 70 pages

- Some organisations concentrated on only one or two issues, while others addressed many issues

- The importance ascribed to any topic by an organisation varied considerably

- Some organisations were largely or totally concerned with the area of the health services in which they themselves are involved, while others took a wider view

- The organisations who responded to the invitation to submit views were self-selected and so do not provide a representative sample.

The percentage of submissions that have dealt with a particular topic is given in table 3. The views and proposals on each theme are described in the chapters that follow.

Table 3: Key areas of change proposed in submissions from organisations:

Theme	Covered in percentage of submissions
Health promotion and illness prevention	49%
Acute care	43%
Funding, eligibility	32%
Quality in health services	32%
The infrastructure of the health system	32%
Community-based health and personal social services	31%
People's experiences of the health services	21%
Health needs of older people	15%
Health needs of people who are excluded or disadvantaged	15%
Health needs of people with mental health difficulties	13%
Health needs of people with physical/sensory disabilities	10%
Health needs of people with learning disabilities	7%

Chapter 1

Health promotion and illness prevention

Introduction

49 per cent of submissions from organisations made specific reference to health promotion and illness prevention. Those who commented were overwhelmingly in favour of developing this aspect of the health services.

Responsibility for promoting public health is seen as resting with many departments and agencies, as highlighted in this comment from the Irish Heart Foundation:

> There is a need for a public health policy with cross-sectoral participation. As stated in the Cardiovascular Strategy, 'the development of a physical and social environment which makes the healthier choice the easier choice' should be a priority for all government and voluntary agencies.

The main aspects of health promotion and illness prevention raised in submissions were the following:

- Health education and health promotion programmes

- Prevention initiatives and screening programmes

- Facilities and incentives for healthy living

- Professional roles in health promotion and illness prevention.

A small number of contributors recommended more research in relation to health promotion and illness prevention programmes.

Health education/health promotion

At a strategic level, there is a need to change the focus from individual health to determinants of health, according to the Regional Health Promotion Managers/Directors of Health Promotion Group. The Group believes that the introduction of health proofing for Government policies would be a positive move in this direction, but is concerned that the focus has remained on individual education strategies. Individually-focused strategies must be supported by measures to change the surrounding environment:

> The predominant emphasis of the health promotion elements of the new Health Strategy should be on population measures, because a small improvement across the whole population is greater than can be achieved through individuals and high-risk targeting. This will mean a shift in thinking, to see health-related behaviour as a social and state responsibility, not one which can be relegated to individuals and families.

Several other contributors take a similarly broad view of health promotion and link it to the concepts of empowerment and personal responsibility. Health status is shaped by many facets of people's lives, so health promotion must engage with the need for structural social change.

The interdependence between health education 'on the ground' and more fundamental structural social change is well described in an extract from the submission from the National Women's Council. Although the point being made refers specifically to women's health, the thrust of the comment reflects a similar view in the submissions relating to people in general:

> The impact of women's social and economic circumstances on their health must be understood. As a consequence of women's experiences of inequality they can be particularly vulnerable to unhealthy social and material circumstances. In order to tackle health inequalities, one cannot assume that everyone has the resources and autonomy to effect the necessary changes in behaviour and lead healthier lives. Emphasis on health education in isolation falls at risk of placing sole responsibility for ill health on particular groups rather than examining greater structural inequalities.

The Council underlines the need to address structural inequalities and to work towards empowering those who are marginalised and socially excluded, as a means of promoting their mental health and well-being.

The Adelaide Hospital Society believes that, as Irish society becomes more affluent, it will be afflicted increasingly by associated diseases. Thus, health promotion should be targeted not only at those areas with social deprivation, but also at the more affluent sectors of our society.

The submissions identify the need for health education and health promotion initiatives for the population as a whole and for special groups. Groups mentioned for whom special health promotion/education initiatives are needed are the following:

- Children

- Older people

- Asylum seekers

- People with disabilities

- People experiencing mental health difficulties

- Prisoners

- Parents

- Recipients of blood

- People who have been abused

- People who have specific conditions, such as strokes, head injuries, diabetes

- Members of the Travelling Community.

Prevention programmes and screening programmes

There is good support in the submissions for investment in the prevention of ill health and premature death.

The National Disease Surveillance Centre underlines the need to prioritise a national strategy for communicable disease control, including immunisation programmes. According to the Centre, the large measles outbreak in 2000 demonstrated the deficiencies in current delivery and uptake of vaccines. Health boards are developing a strategy to address these deficiencies and it will be crucial to ensure that the recommendations are implemented.

One of the most frequently mentioned prevention priorities concerned sexually transmitted diseases. Recent figures demonstrate the re-emergence of sexually transmitted diseases such as chlamydia. There is a need for a complete review of the structures to control these diseases and a sexual health strategy to educate young people in methods of reducing risk, according to the National Disease Surveillance Centre.

Other prevention priorities named in submissions include alcohol and drug abuse, eating disorders, suicide, smoking, road death and injury, accidents at work and domestic violence.

Facilities/incentives for healthy living

The need for a range of improved facilities to enable people to adopt healthier lifestyles is addressed in many submissions. An over-riding concern was the need to promote empowerment and to develop strategies through which people can make real choices about health and take personal responsibility for their health. The submissions call for improved leisure facilities for adults and better play facilities for children; stress management programmes and supports for mental health promotion are needed; good information on healthy lifestyles is one of the key provisions to enable people to make sensible choices about their own health; facilities to promote health and safety at work need to be improved as part of the overall health promotion strategy.

Professional roles in health promotion and illness prevention

A number of submissions propose that health promotion needs to be integrated into the work of all health professionals and that many are being under-utilised in the health promotion/prevention field. These include:

- General practitioners
- Physiotherapists
- Nurses
- Midwives
- Community and hospital pharmacists
- Dermatologists
- Specialist occupational physicians
- Health promotion officers
- Community dieticians
- The ambulance services.

The following extracts demonstrate health professionals' interest in being involved in the health promotion/prevention field:

> There are many missed opportunities for health promotion in out-patient departments, accident and emergency units, GP surgeries, wards and people's homes where professionals, particularly nurses, could provide education for patients if they were up-skilled and supported with up-to-date information. (The Irish Nurses Organisation)

> The healthcare system must now review how best it can utilise pharmacy as a resource in the evolving concept of health promotion in wellness management…An initiative such as 'health promoting pharmacies', akin to 'health promoting hospitals' is long overdue. (The Pharmaceutical Society of Ireland)

Chapter 2

Acute care and maternity services

Introduction

A total of 43 per cent of submissions from organisations made reference to acute care and a further 7 per cent discussed maternity services. The material on maternity services relates to community-based services as well as hospital-based services. A decision was made to include the material in this chapter only, so as to avoid duplication.

The main aspects of acute care covered were the following:

- The need for a new strategic approach to acute/hospital care

- Improved access and resources generally

- Services for people with particular conditions

- Quality of care

- Accident and emergency services

- Research/planning in acute care

- Out-patient services.

A strategy for acute care

Several organisations made the case for a new strategy for acute care. Detailed proposals are contained in some of these submissions, mainly from major providers and representative bodies. Beaumont Hospital, for example, proposes that, in the case of their service, a strategic policy must have regard to the various types of service provided by the hospital – national specialties, sub-specialties and the provision of acute services to people living in the catchment area of the hospital. In the case of each of these, protocols, specific funding mechanisms and development planning are needed.

The Irish Medical Organisation (IMO) provides a very detailed and comprehensive analysis of all aspects of acute hospital care, including hospital financing, manpower planning and training, the role and number of consultants in the hospital service, facilities, bed capacity and specialist acute care for older people.

While focusing on an acute care strategy, there is a view in many submissions that such a strategy must be developed within the context of the wider Health Strategy and in parallel with a strategy for care in the community. The delicate balances to be achieved are underlined in this comment:

There is an urgent need to develop a new hospital strategy for the entire country. However, this hospital strategy cannot be developed without, at the same time, developing a primary and community care strategy. The needs of rural populations have to be addressed within a context that complex high technology care cannot be provided outside urban centres, except through telematics. At the same time, the political context has to be accepted – that hospitals mean jobs and confer status on a community. In developing a new hospital strategy it will therefore be crucial that communities are offered high quality primary and community care services, using existing hospital facilities in an appropriate manner. (Adelaide Hospital Society)

Research/planning for acute care

There was a strong sense emanating from some organisations that the current system of acute care is not based on a firm bedrock of research and planning and the following extracts were typical in this regard:

There is a dearth of health services research relating specifically to the Irish health services, notably in the area of health services management…Similarly, with the Waiting List Initiative where a variety of strategies have been adopted without researching which of them have produced the greatest reduction or indeed what specific factors are contributing to the reduction of waiting lists. (Department of Health Services Management, TCD)

Remarkably, however, no formal Policy review of or guidelines for the Sector have emerged in the past twenty-one years. This has resulted in significant investment in key strategic areas involving Major Hospitals particularly in recent years … proceeding in a policy vacuum. It is considered critically important that future strategies e.g. the provision of increased bed capacity and improved infrastructure in the system etc are underpinned by and progressed within the context of a clear and coherent Policy framework. (St. James's Hospital)

Improved access and resources

Much concern was expressed in submissions about access to acute care and the need to reduce waiting lists. The main proposals for addressing the issue focused on the need for more hospital beds and more hospital staff.

The facilities available, such as technology and theatre facilities, also need to be improved substantially according to submissions.

There was little disagreement within the submissions around this aspect of acute care. One topic, however, on which there was some disagreement related to the issue of 'step-down' facilities. The crucial point of difference here was that while some organisations advocated the development of 'step-down' facilities to 'free up' acute hospital beds, others perceived these as having the potential to be used inappropriately.

Age Action Ireland points out that older people feel they are less important than other patients and seen as 'bed blockers' who are often discharged without proper follow-up services.

While much of the emphasis was on waiting lists, other factors such as hospital location, travel time and transport were seen as important aspects of the access issue.

The absence of transport to and from acute care is seen as a major issue, for older people in particular. It is also a big problem for those on low incomes or with difficulty accessing public transport and people travelling from islands to the mainland. Awareness of transport needs should be integrated into the system of acute care provision. For example, people travelling long distances should not be asked to attend clinics either early or late in the day as this can add greatly to their costs and reduce the uptake of hospital appointments.

The need to decentralise many services now located in large urban hospitals was proposed in several submissions as a means of improving access to services. However, the balance to be achieved between local access and quality is underlined in the submission from the Medical Council:

> In many areas, regionalisation policies within the hospital services are based on a 'flagship' hospital with comprehensive facilities, working in conjunction with a number of district or general hospitals. Unfortunately, examples exist where a regional centre appears not to be in a position to adequately support the surrounding hospitals. Real concerns have therefore arisen about the overall quality of service.

> While the concept of local and accessible service to patients is an admirable one, it must not be provided at the expense of a proper standard of care. Regionalisation policies should reflect a real commitment to integrate the services and structures within a region to a common standard of care.

Services for particular groups

The material on acute hospital provision for particular groups is quite diverse. It covers services for people with many conditions and special needs. The following is an overview of the types of services that are called for:

Services for people with particular conditions

- Oncology services

- Stroke units in every general hospital by 2004

- Improved hospital provision for people with diabetes

- In-patient and out-patient units for people with eating disorders

- Improved provision for children with congenital heart defects

- More emphasis on the importance of palliative care in acute hospitals

- Specialist services for older people.

Services for people with disabilities

- Clinical nurse specialist posts in hospitals to assist people with disabilities

- Improved provision for people with dementia

- Improved provision and co-ordination for people with psychiatric conditions

- Supports in hospitals for people with sensory disabilities.

Services for deprived and marginalised groups

- Translation and other services for refugees

- More Traveller-friendly hospitals

- Improved acute hospital services for women and children experiencing violence by family members.

Children and adolescents in hospital

A number of contributors propose a child and family-friendly ethos in hospitals and pay particular attention to the needs of adolescents in the hospital setting. Children in Hospital Ireland makes the case for a holistic approach to hospital care for children:

> Studies of the interaction between hospitals and sick children have led to the development of principles and practices to provide an environment which is conducive to the promotion of health and the reduction of stress, with the emotional and clinical needs being given appropriate attention.

The organisation goes on to make a very comprehensive set of detailed proposals as to how the well-being of children in hospital can be looked after. These proposals deal with issues that include hospital planning and design, the need for hospital play-specialists, support for parental presence and involvement, the ward environment, ethical issues and consent to treatment, and care of the dying child.

Quality of care

In relation to quality of care in hospitals, a strong emphasis was on improved communication at all levels – communication with the patient, communication among professional staff and improved linkages with personnel involved in community services.

As with the general public, organisations want to see discharge procedures changed and developed, to ensure a smooth transition for the patient from hospital to home or community care and clear arrangements in place for follow-up care.

Higher levels of paramedical involvement are needed in hospitals, according to submissions, as well as facilities for counselling.

Accident and emergency services

Within the wider strategy for acute care, there is a need for a specific strategy addressing accident and emergency services, according to a number of contributors. For example:

> The structure, resources and method of utilisation of resources in A&E units need to be reviewed ensuring real time services for emergencies with appropriate response times and accessibility. This should improve service provision and provide a safer environment for both patients and staff. The creation of admission/observation units should focus on reducing the extent of the demand for acute admissions to the wards at the expense of elective admissions. (IMO)

And

> Care in the Emergency Department must be provided by appropriately trained and supervised staff, working in the right conditions. Hospital inspection teams have repeatedly been concerned that deficiencies in staffing, training or equipment exist in some Departments and have an immediate impact on the quality of care provided to patients.
>
> Individual hospitals have addressed these issues for accreditation purposes but outstanding issues remain. The Medical Council welcomes additional measures such as the appointment of additional consultants in Emergency Medicine to address these deficiencies. (Medical Council)

A point which arose in some submissions around admission policies centred on the question of who should take admission decisions, particularly about emergency admissions. It was argued by some that consideration should be given to the appointment of generalists, as opposed to consultant physicians with special interests, who would act as gatekeepers to the A&E and would refer patients requiring specialist attention after initial investigation and diagnosis. The Consumers Association of Ireland advises that the experimental use of GP services in A&E should be continued.

Compared to the submissions from the general public, the relatively low level of focus on accident and emergency services and out-patients services is noticeable. The submissions from the organisations, as opposed to individuals, suggest a distance from the day-to-day frustration and anger associated with waiting in accident and emergency and out-patient clinics.

Maternity services

Maternity services are raised in 7 per cent of submissions from organisations. Many of the points raised around the background to the current maternity system in Ireland are well captured by the Institute of Obstetricians and Gynaecologists of the Royal College of Physicians of Ireland as follows:

> Over the past 30 years maternal mortality and prenatal mortality have fallen dramatically in Ireland. Ireland has one of the lowest maternal mortality rates in the developed world and our corrected perinatal mortality rate compares favourably with our European partners. These improvements and outcomes have been achieved by a dedicated obstetric and midwifery complement in the face of an increasingly hostile medico-legal environment and an under-resourced service.

The submission from the Joint Standing Committee of three Dublin Maternity Hospitals says that the Coombe, the National Maternity Hospital and the Rotunda are under enormous pressures due to increasing numbers of births, rising patient expectations and unavailability of staff, midwives in particular.

Continuity and choice of care

There should be continuity in the provision of care provided to each woman from early pregnancy right through to postnatal stage.

Antenatal care should be provided in a more flexible way than at present and should be available to women in their own local communities, with midwives having a key role.

The needs and complexities, both legal and otherwise, associated with providing counselling and support for women experiencing crisis pregnancies are the main focus of the detailed submission from the Cork Women's Right to Choose Group.

With regard to postnatal care, there was a view that the current service is inadequate due largely to the fact that this role has fallen mainly to public health nurses whose workload is already too great to allow them to provide the service. The Midwifery Tutor Group recommend that Ireland should have a community postnatal service similar to that offered in the United Kingdom, where a community midwife visits new mothers at home for 10 days after birth and in many cases up to 28 days.

Availability of midwifery services

There is an urgent need to increase the number of student places for trainee midwives and to consider active recruitment strategies to fill these places, according to submissions on this topic. The Midwives Association of Ireland recommends the development of direct entry midwife education programmes.

In the context of developing the attractiveness of midwifery as a career option, the Irish Nurses Organisation (INO) argues that the role and responsibilities of the midwife need to be acknowledged. It also states that the limitations and constraints experienced by midwives in Ireland as a result of the institutionally organised and centralised structures of maternity provision in this country need to be reduced.

Other proposals

In addition to these proposals, there was a range of general proposals, as follows:

- Improvement of maternity services in particular locations

- The need for postnatal mentoring projects (such as community mothers)

- The need for more sensitivity to the cultural issues around maternity services for refugees and asylum seekers (e.g. inappropriateness for women from some ethnic groups of being examined by a male doctor)

- Extended use of videophone networks to link maternity hospitals and thus enhance treatment

- Development of maternity services for women living on islands

- Free, universal access to contraception, fertility treatment and information around choice, sexually-transmitted diseases, HIV and AIDS

- A review of the national policy on breastfeeding

- Development of postnatal care, in particular related to postnatal depression

- Increased involvement of midwives in the management and delivery of maternity care services.

Chapter 3

Funding, equity, eligibility and entitlements

Introduction

Almost a third of organisations (32 per cent) make proposals about issues to do with funding, equity and eligibility for health services. The material in the submissions dealing with the funding of health services is complex. A small number of contributors deal with funding at the 'macro' level, looking at the level of health spending within overall public spending.

Other contributors discuss funding allocations for particular programmes; still others comment on budgetary mechanisms and the consequences of these for service delivery.

Some submissions discuss the relative merits for the consumer of different models of funding and the problems inherent in the Irish system which is based on a mix of taxation and private insurance. The public/private 'mix' and the existence of a 'two-tier' system are discussed in many submissions - usually in terms of the perceived consequences of the current system for fair access to services.

Operational funding issues

A number of organisations and agencies raise operational funding issues relating to both revenue and capital funding.

The Irish Pharmaceutical Healthcare Association is among those calling for a new perspective on health expenditure, in which it would be seen as investment rather than cost and, as such, generate longer term returns. The Association proposes a move to new kinds of budgetary practices that recognise the interdependencies within the health system as a whole. These may require new financial procedures and reorganisation of current systems. The example given draws on the organisation's own sphere of activity:

> There are no advantages for patient welfare or overall health budgeting if spending controls in one area of the health service, for example, drug budgets in primary care, just result in increased costs in other areas of the health budget, for example hospital care.

The Joint Standing Committee of the Dublin Maternity Hospitals offers a detailed analysis of current funding mechanisms, together with recommendations for improving the current arrangements. It makes a case for activity-based costings as a basis for reimbursement, arguing that this will allow agencies to plan effective delivery of services and know that cash flow, pay and non-pay revenues will be secure.

The Association of Hospital Chief Executives recommends an increase in the amount of capital funding to maintain hospital infrastructure and in funding allocations, both revenue and capital, to take account of 'the disproportionate demand for services within the Eastern Region'.

Beaumont Hospital highlights a range of current practices which, in its view, makes financial planning difficult. The Hospital proposes a series of strategic changes:

- Integrate capital and revenue planning

- Funding should take asset depreciation into account

- Provide indicative budgets for a 3-5 year period

- Recognise the extra costs of cross-boundary referrals and of patients with higher level of acuity of need.

The Mater Hospital also makes a series of detailed recommendations about budgeting including a proposal for a change in fiscal policy to permit corporate support for the healthcare system (charity donations).

Among the changes called for by the Bons Secours Health System is recognition of the need for private providers to recover all costs including the cost of capital, to allow them to continue to invest and to provide public services at an economic rate.

According to the Irish Heart Foundation there is a need for a clear statement in relation to funding mechanisms for voluntary organisations. Funding should be allocated in 3-year tranches, which would improve financial accountability and facilitate planning within the voluntary sector. The current system of annual review does not allow sufficient time for strategic development and proper coordination of service provision.

Models and levels of funding

The two main kinds of funding model for healthcare provision which are referred to in submissions are a social insurance-based model and a tax-based model.

Supporters of the social insurance model tend to the view that such a system, whereby all citizens would be equally insured with Government subsidising the less well off, offers the best prospect of delivering an equitable healthcare service.

> ...consideration should be given to a system of universal health insurance to cover a basic healthcare package to which all citizens would be guaranteed equal access. (Irish Pharmaceutical Healthcare Association)

> Accepting that the population is unlikely to accept tax increases, a compulsory health insurance scheme, providing equal benefits to the entire population, should be introduced. (Adelaide Hospital Society)

> ...a social insurance payment scheme to cover primary care, with premiums for those on low incomes paid by the State. (Diabetes Federation)

However, a common theme running through many submissions is that no one system is perfect and that changing the method of funding may not be in itself the answer. A fundamental problem with regard to equity is seen by many as the lack of capacity in the healthcare system, which can only be addressed by increasing overall levels of funding. A number of submissions make the case for a higher proportion of Gross Domestic Product (GDP) to be spent on healthcare. While the absolute level of spending on health has increased significantly, the decrease as a percentage of GDP is noted.

The public/private mix

As already noted, most submissions comment on the current 'mix' in terms of equity and access issues. The thrust of the views is that poor people and disadvantaged groups are faring badly under the current arrangements. It appears that the public/private mix has become virtually synonymous with the concept of a 'two-tier' system'.

In its analysis, the Society of St. Vincent de Paul identifies several linked factors which, in its view, make the current operation of the 'mix' unacceptable in its outcomes for the public patient. The Society identifies the public/private bed mix in public hospitals and the manner in which consultants' public contracts/private practice mix operates, as factors contributing to the severe problems experienced by public patients.

There is a strong view that any new arrangements must result in fair and equitable access, based on need. A small number of submissions propose that in future arrangements, the private healthcare sector should operate separately from the public sector, with no access by private patients to public facilities. Others call for a review of the operation of the consultants' common contract to ensure greater equity for public patients. Most tend to concentrate on proposing improvements in entitlements (see below) for public patients, rather than envisaging radical new models of funding/care.

Some submissions comment on strategic policy and management issues relating to the public/private 'mix.' In the main, these observations and proposals come from private providers of healthcare. These submissions raise and discuss the following issues, among others:

- The need for an internally coherent strategy around the 'mix'

- The case for a fundamental re-evaluation of the role of Government in healthcare provision, e.g the case for Government to relinquish its monopoly over the supply of beds

- The development of formal public-private partnerships to address the shortfall in hospital services

- The case for 'national mobilisation' of all public and private healthcare resources to meet current needs

- The need for closer co-ordination between public and non-public services and recognition of both as integral elements of provision.

The case is made by a number of private providers for extension of private services to deliver specialisms such as hospice services, services for people with dementia and services for young people with chronic illness. There are also calls for private hospitals to be licensed to operate accident and emergency services.

Changes in eligibility/entitlements

Several organisations call for a rights-based approach to service entitlements for the population in general. Some propose statutory entitlements for particular groups, such as older people. Most proposals deal with enhancements to existing levels of entitlement.

Comhairle challenges a distinction between eligibility and entitlement. It argues that a person who is eligible for a service should be entitled to it. Comhairle is also concerned that national guidelines and legislation to deal with entitlement to community care services have not been drawn up, for example, in relation to home helps. It is concerned that having a formal entitlement to a service, such as dental services, does not mean that a person will get a service, and suggests that legislation should either withdraw the entitlement or deliver on it.

The Community and Voluntary Pillar make a series of detailed recommendations in relation to the General Medical Scheme (GMS). Their proposals include the application of national eligibility criteria to remove inconsistencies between health board areas and the setting up of an independent body to administer the Scheme.

Entitlements should be strategically managed so as to support the policy objective of shifting the focus in the health services to primary care and the integration of community and hospital services, according to contributors. For example, the Diabetes Federation suggests the need to remove the incentive to choose hospital care over GP care. The Federation makes a general point about access and eligibility:

Access to professional advice should not be influenced by eligibility or by the setting in which care is provided. Patients should not have to pay for community podiatry, for example, when this service is inadequate or unavailable in the clinic.

Medical card entitlement

Concern was expressed about the real decline in the proportion of the population with a medical card.

The main proposals regarding changes in arrangements for medical card entitlement are:

- Provision of medical cards to further groups of people
- Increase in eligibility limits
- Access for medical card holders to an enhanced range of services with the medical card
- Alignment of family entitlement to a medical card with the Family Income Supplement.

The provision of medical cards for children was proposed in several submissions. For example, the submission from the Children's Rights Alliance suggests a phased introduction:

Medical card income eligibility guidelines must be increased to extend coverage to more children in households of low income, including those on the national minimum wage.

Medical cards should be provided for all children on a phased basis, initially for all children under the age of 5 and ultimately for all children and young people under the age of 18.

A substantially similar view is held by Barnardos. The National Youth Council wishes to see the medical card extended to all young people under 18 years and those in further education. As well as these national bodies, many locally-based organisations make similar proposals.

Many additional groups make the case for having access to free medical care, irrespective of income because of disability, chronic illness or social circumstances. The main reason given in the case of groups with particular chronic illnesses is the frequency with which they tend to need to visit the GP. Among such groups are people with asthma, people with Alzheimer's disease, all those with a disability, people with stoma, all those with long-term illness, families with recurrent medical expenses and family carers. A particular case is made for flexibility in relation to medical card access for women living in violent relationships who may not have access to money.

Several organisations recommend extending the range of services available through the medical card to include complementary health services, counselling, contraception, fertility treatment, all medical needs and equipment, access to the most effective medications and free continence wear for medical card holders who avail of private nursing home care.

Other entitlements

Comhairle proposes a new entitlement - a subsidy towards GP costs for certain groups.

Extensions to the Long-Term Illness Scheme are proposed. The proposals include suggestions that a specified number of GP visits should be refunded under this scheme, in a given time period. There are also many proposals to extend the cover of the scheme to further groups – people with chronic mental illness, people with spinal injury, people with kidney disease, for example.

There were very few comments about the Drugs Payment Scheme. The Knocknacarra Active Retirement Association believes that, while the scheme is good for families, for a retired person with no medical card, £42 per month represents a large proportion of one's pension.

Other entitlement issues

The Working Group on Code of Practice for Sheltered Work makes a detailed case for people with disabilities in receipt of social welfare benefits to be allowed to retain their medical card on entering employment and People with Disabilities in Ireland (PwDI) argues that people with disabilities should be assessed only on their own income for eligibility.

The Refugee Council similarly raises the 'poverty trap' in which refugees and asylum seekers may find themselves. The Council is also concerned about the time lag between the point of arrival in the country and receipt of a medical card.

The problems experienced by Travellers on account of difficulties in transferring from area to area (and similar difficulties for homeless people) are raised. A simplified system along the lines of that being developed in the Eastern Region is recommended.

There are proposals concerning benefits paid by the Department of Social, Community and Family Affairs. The most frequently mentioned is the Carer's Allowance, where the case is made for a non-means tested allowance for family carers. The case is also made for increasing the allowance of £10 per week which unemployed or low income families receive towards the cost of pre-school/crèche facilities.

Chapter 4

Quality in health services

Introduction

Organisations paid considerable attention to the issue of quality management throughout the health and personal social services sector, with almost one third (32 per cent) making proposals on this matter.

The main emphasis in this material is on ways of improving quality through the adoption or enhancement of quality management systems and accountability systems.

Proposals for permanent structures for consultation are also described in this chapter, because of the role envisaged in the submissions for all stakeholders in standard setting and evaluation.

Much of the commentary on quality services in submissions is linked to human resource issues such as staffing levels, training and staff development. This material is described in the following chapter.

Quality systems

Many complex and technical matters were raised in submissions regarding systems for quality management, accountability and risk management. Quality systems are seen primarily as a way of securing better outcomes for service users, but there is also a focus on efficiency in resource management.

Quality assurance systems, systematic use of guidelines, standards and evidence-based protocols are needed in all healthcare settings, according to contributors.

The Medical Council notes good progress in the implementation of competence assurance structures for doctors. However, the Council envisages the need for a legislative base for these structures. The Council is also concerned about EU structures for quality assurance. The Council draws a clear distinction between competence assurance systems, which address the capabilities of individual doctors and Quality Assurance (QA) systems that deal with quality in services. The development of clinical governance offers a framework for QA systems to complement professional systems, according to the Council.

Speaking specifically about hospital services, the IMO points to linkages between quality, availability and affordability and the difficulty of achieving all three simultaneously. The role of evidence-based practice in supporting decision-making is noted:

> The development of evidence-based medical practice is a natural counter-weight to the uncritical adoption of expensive new developments. It needs to become an integral part of Irish hospitals' practice, along with Quality Assurance Review and other audit programmes.

Sources of quality measures

How are measures of quality to be derived? The proposals as to the sources of quality measures vary enormously and address many different kinds of healthcare provision. They range from high-level statutory regulation, to processes of dialogue and sharing of experience and information among providers.

The Pharmaceutical Society refers to ongoing work on legislative reform which, it hopes, 'will address a number of the current deficiencies that exist in the regulation of pharmaceutical practice, including the introduction of fitness-to-practice provisions and the equal application of controls over service delivery in both the primary and secondary healthcare environments.'

The Society sees this kind of legislative framework for professional practice as critical to the quality agenda:

> *Fundamental to the delivery of appropriate healthcare is the ability to ensure professional competency to effectively control and monitor professional practice and take appropriate action when required. Essential to the achievement of this is a framework of appropriate and relevant legislation.*

VHI suggests the need for a standardised approach to the licensing of healthcare facilities along the lines of the Radiological Protection Institute model, as a way of ensuring uniform basic quality.

Accreditation arrangements and systems are also seen as critical to the achievement of quality. For example:

> *…Accreditation, based on continuous quality improvement principles, sets the overarching context within which quality endeavours pertinent to specific elements of and participants in (e.g. functions, systems, users, professions, etc) the system can be fashioned, developed and pursued. (St. James's Hospital)*

Other mechanisms proposed in submissions include:

- Physician-led standards and protocols, with standing committees involving external expert representation

- Sharing of information on international best practice

- Sharing of information on inter-hospital comparisons on a confidential basis and annual savings plans in which savings are retained for improved care (specifically with regard to efficiencies)

- Protocols agreed with national professional bodies as the basis of quality monitoring

- Benchmarking of community services, including mental health services

- Development of total quality management cycles

- A primary care equipment strategy, including training strategy for clinical engineers.

While the main emphasis seems to be on standards derived from professional practice and inter-professional dialogue, some submissions refer to the role of service users in the development of standards, both in individual healthcare facilities and at national level. For example, there is a proposal for the setting up of a forum of stakeholders to draw up plans for the licensing of healthcare facilities as well as addressing other issues of mutual interest.

The need for quality standards for particular groups is addressed. According to submissions, quality standards and quality management are needed to guarantee the particular interests of children, children in care, older people in residential care, people with learning disabilities in residential care, people with mental illness, people in workshop settings.

Data gathering for quality management

The need for data gathering strategies for quality management is underlined in several submissions. More robust strategies are needed, it is argued, to support the development of evidence-based protocols and other instruments. The National Health Information Strategy is seen as particularly important in this context.

Mechanisms are needed for the sharing of information about eHealth and IT projects. For example, the INO is concerned about the absence of ways to share the outcomes and experience from many information projects being undertaken around the country:

> However, each organisation/individual is working in isolation with little or no dialogue across organisations, or between individuals. Accessing information about these projects is dependent on informal contacts or in conversation with colleagues.

> As these projects are in their infancy, it would be opportune to set up some system of partnership and sharing of information, facilitating consistency, but avoiding duplication and resource inefficiency, whilst maintaining individuality.

The INO proposes that the Department of Health and Children should appoint a central co-ordinator to advise and disseminate information in healthcare informatics.

Accountability, risk management

The need for statutory and published forms of accountability is raised.

St. James's Hospital seeks clarification of the respective accountabilities and legal responsibilities of governance, management and clinical governance. Their submission suggests that 'vagueness or ambivalence with respect to corporate body status of agencies is now legally dangerous and untenable' and recommends that the instruments establishing corporate bodies need comprehensive review.

Patient Focus, the national voluntary patient advocacy organisation, underlines the role of the public in relation to accountability, risk management and quality assurance. The following extract highlights this view:

> The public are not only service users, they are also the owners, stakeholders and paymasters of our health services. Accountability gives credence to the phrase 'our health services'. It isn't a negative thing, as it is shared (patients are accountable too) and it encourages and feeds on co-operation at all levels. It also prevents expensive negative defensive practice on the part of professionals and litigation on behalf of patients.

The submission calls for the following actions:

- Encourage publication of service reports

- Arrange meetings to explain incidents to patients/families

- Develop a culture of incident reporting and evaluation for possible lessons

- Use communication tools to extend any useful lessons throughout the service.

Permanent processes for consultation and participation

A lot of attention was paid in submissions to the importance of ongoing consultation and participation in the design, planning, monitoring and evaluation of healthcare and health services.

Many submissions acknowledge the extent of the commitment to partnership. The responses to current initiatives and practices are positive.

The submissions call for a level of involvement beyond the gathering of views by public servants. They envisage participative structures through which citizens, communities and service users engage with the State in the planning, development and evaluation of services.

National partnership/participation

The overarching policy context for consultation is the national partnership process, as exemplified in the arrangements for National Agreement negotiations.

The significance of this partnership approach at national level is expressed in this extract from the SIPTU submission:

> *Partnership must continue to be the cornerstone of the change and improvement processes in the health system. This means deepening partnership at national and local levels through the involvement of more staff on a wider range of issues and by the resourcing of those activities taking place under the heading of partnership.*

> *Partnership should extend to all stakeholders, most importantly, the current and potential users of health services. Long-term commitment is needed for partnership at all levels to bring about the necessary change to reform the health system.*

Regional and community consultation

At regional level, there is some discussion of the kinds of representation people want in the work of health boards, both at governance level and in sub-structures. Many groups say they need direct representation. The submissions argue for direct representation for people with disabilities and their representative bodies, parent representatives, women and older people.

Clondalkin Partnership suggests that health boards should move out to communities and consult directly with them.

A statutory underpinning for consultation at community level is recommended by Age Action Ireland who recommend the setting up of community councils at regional and county levels in all health boards. The councils would have a statutory right to be consulted on the planning, provision and evaluation of the health and social services in each health board.

Participation needs skills, capacities and mechanisms. This point is highlighted in the submission from the Community Workers Co-Operative, which makes the case for resources to help the Community and Voluntary Sector to involve people who are marginalised. The empowerment concept is captured in this extract from their submission:

> *The community sector should not be mediated but facilitated. There is a danger of relying on partnership structures and internal personnel to bring forward social exclusion interests. This approach runs counter to commitments re the right of local communities to organise and represent their own interests.*

Consultation and partnership with particular groups

There was a good deal of material in submissions about consultation with particular groups.

The effectiveness of some current structures is mentioned. For example, Positive Action believes that the consultation process undertaken in planning services for women affected with Hepatitis C as a result of receiving Anti-D Immunoglobulin is a model that could be followed in the health services generally. Pavee Point, in describing the *Primary Healthcare for Travellers* project, points to the value of their partnership with the health board and sees it as an effective model that is impacting positively on the health condition of Travellers in the pilot area. The National Women's Council finds that the inclusion of representatives on Women's Health Advisory Committees 'has been a key development in mainstreaming women's representation within the health services'.

The National Council on Ageing and Older People sees the Health Strategy as an opportunity to develop a coherent and formalised policy and strategy for consulting users of health and social services. The Council makes a specific proposal in relation to consultation with older people:

> The Council recommends that Advisory Committees on the elderly, recommended in The Years Ahead (1988), should be reviewed and given an extended remit to incorporate the function of consulting with older people. This would entail revising the composition of the committees to include older people themselves. The revised committees could then act as Advisory Committees on Services for Older People. All user groups should be represented on such committees.

The National Youth Council points to the importance of respecting the views of children and young people and links the experience of consultation with the development of civic responsibility, positive mental health and skill development among young people:

> Young people and children have a body of experience and knowledge that is unique to their situation. They have views and ideas as a result of that experience. Yet there is frequently a failure to recognise the legitimacy of their contribution to decision-making. Consulting young people and drawing on their perceptions, knowledge and ideas are essential to the development of effective public policy.

Consultation at agency level

Several submissions discuss the need for consultation with service users within the agency providing services to them. They should be involved in service monitoring and evaluation. Formal structures may be needed to promote this. Comhar, the Adult Counselling Service, proposes minimum standards for service user involvement and believes it may be necessary to establish this consultation on a statutory basis, in order to embed it in health service delivery.

Chapter 5

Human resources

Introduction

The wide-ranging issues relating to human resources and human resource management in the healthcare system receive much attention in submissions. The importance of the human resource agenda is underlined in this observation from SIPTU:

A proper Human Resource Plan is needed to support any new health strategy. Strategies may come and go, but the people who are an integral resource to the health system need to be appreciated, developed, motivated and effectively managed with respect and dignity if the desired vision, values, goals and objectives are to become a reality.

The IPA Health Sector Advisory Group concludes its analysis of the environment for human resources in the healthcare sector by pointing to the need for a recognised HR infrastructure:

An overall theme emerging from this consideration is the importance of effective HR policies and practices in the future health services, especially the recognition that HR (rather than personnel administration) is a key specialisation and the need for health service organisations to have an internal organisation development resource.

Among the wide range of issues to be included within such a human resources strategy, according to submissions, are recruitment, retention of staff, staff motivation, an examination of skill-mix issues to ensure effective resource use, a culture of openness and transparency in services, health, well-being and safety of staff, insurance cover for healthcare personnel, childcare, working hours, pay and staff morale.

The main areas of human resources dealt with in submissions are:

- Staffing levels

- Health, safety and well-being of staff

- Training and development

- Industrial relations.

Staffing levels

Not surprisingly, staffing levels attract much comment and are the subject of several very detailed recommendations. For example, the INO describes in detail the factors it sees as having contributed to present nursing shortages. The INO makes a range of proposals about nursing manpower including the establishment of a manpower forum partnership to address the issue of nursing shortages. It also proposes a process for long-term planning:

The introduction, at Department of Health level, of a nursing manpower planning department which would, in consultation with individual employing authorities, provide 3-, 5- and 10-year nursing manpower strategies, inclusive of appropriate education to meet the specific health service needs, e.g. theatre nursing.

The IMO, similarly, makes comprehensive proposals relating to medical manpower planning at all levels of the healthcare system. One of the concerns raised is the need to address the intrinsic links between manpower planning, postgraduate training and service delivery strategies. The issue is reflected in this extract concerning hospital manpower:

The issues of manpower planning and postgraduate training have been much debated in recent years. There can be no sensible plan relating to manpower and training unless we have clearly defined how we plan to develop the hospital service. If we ignore either half of this two-sided equation we risk creating chaos. There should be critical appraisal of all proposed changes to numbers, to the role of interns, to changes in specialist training, in the light of their potential effects on service delivery to patients. The training bodies do not see service delivery as their primary concern but the Department of Health should see it as theirs.

As well as addressing medical staffing in hospitals and community, the IMO looks in detail at issues for doctors employed within the public health system at all levels and makes wide-ranging recommendations on career structures, career development and working conditions.

Comhairle na n-Ospidéal underlines the need for a more co-ordinated approach to hospital manpower planning. It reiterates the need for more consultants and for non-consultant hospital doctors (NCHDs). Comhairle believes that this will contribute significantly to the further development of high quality and safe services for patients and a coherent, structured career pathway for all hospital doctors.

There are calls in the submissions for increased staffing levels across the board in community services, hospital and other healthcare services. As well as major groups of staff, there are calls for increases in the number of community-based psychologists, extra hospital chaplains, hospital pharmacists and dieticians.

In the area of medical consultants, there is a need, according to submissions, for increased numbers of geriatricians, neurologists, community paediatricians, rehabilitation consultants and obstetricians, among others, as well as the development of an infrastructure for dermatology services around the country. Staffing levels in respect of all the various professions working in obstetrical services and midwifery need to be enhanced.

While much of the emphasis is on staffing levels, attention is also given in some submissions to the question of roles, role definitions and the need to maximise the effective use of personnel in various positions in the health services, so as to allow for the emergence of new and innovative applications of the skills base in the sector. Among the roles discussed are nursing roles, the potential of the role of pharmacists in many areas within the community, such as delivery of health information, the potential role of hospital chaplains as part of a holistically orientated healthcare team in the hospital and the role of community welfare officers.

Recruitment systems

Some submissions discuss selection and recruitment systems in the health services. There is a call from SIPTU for an overhaul of the recruitment and selection system. Challenges in relation to recruitment and retention of personnel are also discussed at some length by the IPA Health Sector Advisory Group. This submission draws attention to a report from Dixon and Baker (1996) which highlighted 'an urgent need to overhaul the recruitment and selection system' and made recommendations for such improvements. The Group believes that the problems identified in that report have become more acute in the interim.

Pay

The following extract from the IMPACT submission looks at principles to underpin pay policy:

> Health sector employment should continue to be about commitment and motivation, but it is
> unrealistic to expect that pay and conditions will not be an overriding factor from the point of view
> of attracting, retaining and rewarding staff. There should be an acceptance that the health service
> should represent a career for all those who enter it. This should apply to clerical/administrative staff
> and non-nursing staff as much as to health professionals and doctors...
>
> As a rule the rates of pay and conditions of employment for health workers should be in line with
> those for workers in good private sector employment. This was the old principle which governed the
> setting of public service pay. There has been a tendency by government to seek to weaken this
> approach. Given the need to ensure high calibre staff in the health sector it is imperative that this
> principle be restored and upheld.

Health, safety and well-being

Several submissions call for comprehensive programmes to ensure the health, safety and well-being of those
who work in the Irish health service. Such a programme would have many facets, including screening
programmes, regular medical and other consultations, various health promotion initiatives, free treatment,
stress management, anti-bullying workshops and recreational facilities on site. 'No fault' insurance cover for
nurses would contribute to their well-being.

The need to audit and monitor the physical environment in which staff work is raised. The Health Services
Employers Agency (HSEA) takes up this point:

> ...it is worthwhile noting that the physical environment in which people work is a key determinant
> of their morale and well-being. Employers therefore should also be urged, in so far as it is
> practicable, to make the necessary financial investments to ensure good physical environments for
> their employees, including their offices or other accommodation, cloakrooms, canteens and quality
> of food.

Training and development

Training and development are linked in submissions both to the process of achieving high quality services for
the public and also to the need to provide opportunities for healthcare personnel to enhance their skills and
promote career development. It is seen as a way of valuing both service user and service provider.

The focus of the material on training and development is mainly on in-career training for personnel at all
levels. Submissions from some providers of postgraduate medical training deal in depth with that facet of
national skill development needs.

Continuing staff development and career development

A strategy for continuing staff development and career development is seen as an essential part of the process
of securing quality outcomes for the public as well as enhancing the motivation and capacity of staff. An
infrastructure for this aspect of health service development is proposed. This infrastructure would cover, for
example, budgetary allocation and the provision of time for training.

The principle of equity in the allocation of training and development resources is seen by IMPACT as an important principle to underpin a training and development strategy:

> There is a need to establish adequate budgets and staff development programmes for all groups of staff. At present the distribution of those resources which are available is seen as inequitable. For instance, clerical/administrative staff perceive that there has been a focus on investing in groups such as nurses, to their exclusion. The particular development plans may need to take account of the circumstances of various groups and there should be focus on training within normal working hours where possible.

The submissions focus on the training needs of many groups within the healthcare system and on many kinds of skill development. Among the areas/groups mentioned are the following:

- Counselling and pastoral care skills for all those dealing directly with service users

- Staff relations, listening skills

- Working with refugees and asylum seekers

- Working in a multi-cultural environment

- Working with women or men who have experienced violence

- Supporting people who have been bereaved and especially those bereaved through suicide

- Co-ordinated training for all health professionals in relation to health promotion

- Training for working with children in hospital

- Training for dealing with continence problems as part of a range of nurse education programmes

- Training for governance.

Some submissions focused on the area of management and leadership development. In its submission, the IPA Health Sector Advisory Group examines the modern challenges for health service managers and the responses and capabilities needed. Listing strategic management, inter-organisational working and performance management among the capabilities needed by managers, the need for new skills in working with people is also highlighted:

> Interestingly, the strong emphasis in the group's thinking was on the necessity to develop interpersonal skills of people, rather than the knowledge base. This is reflective of the changed working environment of staff and the necessity to operate confidently in very different work settings both internally and externally.

The submission calls for a new style of management development, explicitly linked to organisational strategy, organisational development and organisational learning.

The Institute for Public Health highlights the need for leadership development and partnership working:

> Given the broad range of determinants of health, partnership working will be essential to draw together and harness the best possible response from different departments and sectors.

With regard to nurses in particular, the Empowerment of Nurses and Midwives Steering Group highlights the need for management development for nurses.

Postgraduate training

Several submissions focus on the need for increased investment in postgraduate medical education and training and make links between such investment and the capacity of the health system to offer a high quality service. The link between postgraduate training and the retention of doctors and nurses in Ireland is also made.

The Faculty of Health Sciences in Trinity College argues that there has been a lack of investment in the indigenous infrastructure for academic aspects of the health sciences at postgraduate level.

The case is made for 'unbundling' the differing roles of universities in respect of education, research and service delivery, resolution of the 'limbo' between the Department of Health and Children and the Department of Education and Science in which postgraduate academic training resides and recognition of the need for capital as well as recurrent funding for clinical teaching, undergraduate and postgraduate education:

> …there are serious problems with regard to the clinical education/training and practical placement of students in almost all sectors of the health sciences. The solution to these will require capital investment and the appointment of clinical teachers and educators in almost all sectors…It is highly unlikely and improbable that the Higher Education Authority will take the lead in these areas and certainly there is no evidence that it intends or plans to do so. Therefore, it is vital that the Strategy addresses the chronic problems of clinical training, clinical education, postgraduate education and capital development within this sector.

One of the areas examined by the Postgraduate Medical and Dental Board is the usage of training posts within the service delivery environment in hospitals:

> Training posts are primarily for training. Provision of the bulk of service by trainees rotating through jobs at regular intervals is unsatisfactory for patient care and trainees.

The submission goes on to make recommendations about the role of trainees within hospital staffing structures:

> The current medical hierarchy of Consultant, Registrar, Senior House Officer and Intern is based on a larger number of trainees than trained doctors. The provision of medical services by trained doctors will mean changes in work practices with greater emphasis on team work and shared responsibility. There should be a clear vision for trainees in any new medical configuration/model, including in particular the respective roles and functions of consultants and specialists therein.

The submission from St. James's Hospital makes the case for the teaching role of the teaching hospitals to be made explicit and for a funding and accountability strategy to be developed around that role.

Industrial relations

Industrial relations mechanisms are raised in a small number of submissions. The HSEA focuses on the need for both staff and management to commit to the resolution of disputes and differences through established industrial relations machinery and for management and unions to agree comprehensive procedures to cover all issues that could lead to disputes.

The HSEA appraises the industrial relations complexities that exist in the health service environment. The Agency links a positive industrial relations climate with effective policies and procedures to deal with grievances, the need for line managers to be equipped to implement those policies and the importance of strong mechanisms for both career development and performance management.

Chapter 6

Community-based health and personal social services

Introduction

The need for enhanced community-based health services is raised in 31 per cent of the submissions from organisations. The key themes running through the submissions are:

- The need for enhanced levels of a wide range of community services

- Local availability of services

- The need for linkages and connections within and between services, so as to create a holistic, seamless, people-centred service.

There was concern for rural communities and for communities that have special access problems, such as island people. The infrastructure, or lack of infrastructure, to facilitate access is raised regularly – in particular the absence of rural transport systems.

Enhanced levels of service

Organisations identify many community services that need to be developed. As well as wanting to see more services coming on stream, they want those services to 'hang together' to provide a cohesive community service. The main service areas raised were the following:

- Carer support

- General practitioner services

- Community health personnel and health centres

- Pharmaceutical services

- Complementary medicine

- Counselling

- Services for particular population groups.

Carer support

Contributors describe the emotional, physical and financial costs of caring and make the case for greater recognition of those costs. In the absence of comprehensive and flexible supports, caring takes its toll on the health, well-being and family income of the carer. Many carers, especially those in rural areas, experience isolation and can experience increased stress as a result.

The main thrust of the submissions is the need for a cohesive, coherent and broadly-based strategy for carer support. The benefit of such a strategy is summed up in the following contribution from Care Alliance Ireland:

> We need a Government Strategy for carers from the Department of Health. This would lead to statutory rights for carers and set down uniform standards for all health boards. It would encompass all carers, not just carers of older people.
>
> It is vital that carers are supported in the work that they do. They provide essential care for many thousands of people. The cost of this support is significant, but when compared with the cost of replacing carers with formal institutions it is negligible. The Government has a duty to provide this support.

Contributors name the community services they see as essential for carers. The main services named are the following:

* Respite care

* Day care centres

* Free home-help for all family carers

* Non-means testing of the Carer's Allowance

* More home-help hours

* Easier access to aids and appliances

* Information on rights and entitlements

* Support for carer support groups

* Counselling for carers.

Training for all carers, including family carers, is recommended, particularly in relation to lifting and handling and in the proper use of aids and appliances. Contributors want these supports to be provided in a flexible way, responsive to individual needs and circumstances. For example, this might mean helping with laundry, bathing or diet. Such flexible help could avoid the need for residential care. One contributor recommends an individualised support plan for each carer and the person they care for.

More services should come to the home rather than bringing the person to the service. As well as more visits from public health nurses, consultants, physiotherapists and other professionals should make home visits. This would help them to make a more informed assessment of client need. Regular assessment visits are proposed in one submission:

> We recommend monthly visits by GP or practice nurses to assess the patient's condition. This would include a physical assessment, emotional assessment, physiological assessment, dietary assessment and home assessment. This would help to keep people at home and identify problems that can be dealt with. (Bandon Community Hospital)

In the case of people who are terminally ill, the Hospice Foundation recommends that a post of care assistant be provided, with training for those undertaking the work. A pilot scheme along these lines is being undertaken by the Foundation. A pilot project on needs assessment of carers and care recipients in Mayo is described by Caring for Carers Ireland.

General practitioner services

Access to GP services is seen as a core facet of medical care and treatment and key to the maintenance of good health and well-being.

Submissions call for the appointment of more GPs. They also want to see changes in the way GP services are organised and delivered. The importance of developing group practices and other aspects of the general practice infrastructure is highlighted in several submissions. GP services could be part of a more broadly-based community health service, operating out of a primary health centre in the local community, as in this proposal:

> *A number of pilot combined group GP practices should physically be located in the same primary health centre with a range of the community professionals. GPs should have access in these primary health centres to physiotherapy, counselling, nurses etc. (Band Three Directors of Nursing)*

A theme running through the submissions is that improved GP services will enable people to avail of local services and free up hospitals to treat more serious cases. There will be significant cost implications, as pointed out in the submission from the IMO:

> *Additional spending on general practice infrastructure, staffing and equipment, is required to control demand for hospital services. Direct access to diagnostic and treatment procedures are essential if general practice is to provide and be seen to provide, an equivalent standard of service to the hospitals. This should not be confined to GMS practices and will be beyond the capacity of current savings schemes.*

In its submission, BUPA proposes front-loaded investment to overcome barriers to the establishment of GP group practices, including more practices funded by private medical insurance, providing a spectrum of primary, preventive and rehabilitative services.

There is a need for improved GP cover at night and weekends and more time for people on individual visits. The Consumers Association of Ireland suggests a financial incentive for night visits.

Improved GP access to test facilities and test results is recommended. Unacceptable delays in the provision of blood test results to GPs is raised in a small number of submissions.

Contributors raise concern about the lack of choice of GP for medical card holders and for people living on the islands. The need for financial incentives for GPs working in deprived areas is raised. One local group asks why a person's own GP cannot attend them in the community hospital, as it understands this practice is facilitated in many other hospitals.

Community health personnel, community health centres

The case is made in several submissions for increases in the numbers and kinds of community health personnel working at local level:

- Public health nurses

- Practice nurses

- Physiotherapists, occupational therapists and speech and language therapists

- People offering medical specialisms at community level

- Community health workers

- Women's health development officers

- Health psychologists.

Several organisations draw attention to the community service needs of special groups. For example, the Council for Children's Hospitals' Care makes the case for a higher level of community paediatric medicine, including paediatric nurses and ancillary services. GP-based asthma clinics and asthma nurses are proposed by the Asthma Society. The Women's Health Council proposes the development of women's health centres and models of health services that are women-friendly.

Contributors make the case for a new kind of health centre, offering a comprehensive range of primary healthcare services, including screening and developmental checks.

Improved access to locally-delivered primary care of this kind would shift the locus of some forms of care from hospital to community. In local drop-in centres, for example, minor injuries and non-emergency care could be provided. These centres would operate flexible hours, on a seven-day week basis, responsive to local need:

> *An important point to make in the context of developing a patient-centred health service is the need*
> *to develop the provision of routine services outside the Monday to Friday 9am to 5pm slot which*
> *may be very difficult for patients to meet in our increasingly 'time-poor' society. Clearly, one cannot*
> *place unacceptable burdens on individual healthcare professionals, but in the context of increased*
> *staffing, group practices and more flexible rostering, it should prove possible. (Irish Pharmaceutical*
> *Healthcare Association)*

It is suggested in a submission that advanced nurse practitioners could be employed to deal with minor injuries and as part of the staffing of GP group practices.

The Institute of Community Health Nursing believes the work of public health nurses should continue to be organised on a geographic basis rather than linked to GP practices but with greater equity in caseloads. The Institute sees the need for trained care assistants who would be delegated responsibility for provision of basic care, such as bathing and dressing.

The Medical Laboratory Scientists Association believes that consideration should be given to the establishment of laboratories specifically to serve the distinct needs of community-based users such as GPs, public health nurses and other healthcare professionals.

The need for a comprehensive community-based health service is particularly pressing in rural areas. More public health nurses with specific training in areas such as paediatric care, maternity and geriatric care, as well as in various screening processes are needed in these areas. The needs of island people for access to comprehensive community medical services are raised. Comdháil Oileáin na hÉireann makes a detailed and comprehensive proposal for island services, covering health clinic services, resident nursing service and general practice, as part of a broadly based islands healthcare provision plan.

The absence of rural transport is intrinsically linked with access to services. The lack of transport presents difficulties for people wishing to attend clinics, carers who are dependent on others for transport, people with disabilities, mothers of young children, island people and people being discharged from hospital. There are calls for the establishment of rural transport schemes and for the extension of successful pilot schemes.

Pharmaceutical services

Four issues are raised in submissions concerning pharmaceutical services:

• The strategic potential and role of community pharmacists

• Access to pharmaceutical services

• Control of medicines

• The cost of drugs.

The central role of the community pharmacist is described by the Irish Pharmaceutical Union (IPU):

> *The pharmacist is often the first and sometimes the only point of contact for patients seeking advice on the health services, health education and the appropriate use of over-the-counter medication. Thus access to a community pharmacy service can help to maintain good health, as well as providing pharmaceutical care through the provision of advice and medicines. For many in such communities, a local pharmacy is as much a local key service as the local post office or bank.*

The IPU makes the case for the role and expertise of the pharmacist and the strategic development of pharmaceutical care to be explicitly recognised and developed in the Health Strategy.

A number of contributors argue for easier access to community pharmacy, provision of pharmacy services in health centres, access to 'over-the-counter' products in island health centres and relaxation of pharmacy licensing. The IPU believes that the Health (Community Pharmacy Contractor Agreement) Regulations, 1996 have ensured better distribution of services and extension of services to rural areas and hopes to see this trend continue.

With regard to medicines management, the submission from the Irish Medicines Board details strategic changes that the Health Strategy should cover, including the introduction of a statutory system for control of unauthorised medicinal products.

The IPU proposes the development of a pharmaceutical care service that would provide for the continuous monitoring of patient response to prescribed medicines:

> *Currently there is a gap in patient care, in that, once a patient has obtained prescribed medicine from a pharmacy, there is no active assessment procedure to see if the medication is producing the desired effect...under a pharmaceutical care service, the patient's pharmacy will remain in communication with the patient, to establish if they are experiencing any problems with their medication and, in consultation with the doctor, will advise on what action should be taken...It is clear that such a system provides the optimum benefit for the patient and ensures that prescribed medication is used in the most effective way. This is an important factor in reducing admissions to hospital or residential care.*

Proposals are also made by the IPU for a pilot medicines management programme focused on older people and other vulnerable groups and proposals relating to the sale of paracetamol and the distribution of vaccines through pharmacies.

With regard to the cost of medicines, there is a call for the Department of Health and Children to target pharmaceutical companies to ensure that the cost of 'over-the counter' medicines is kept as low as possible.

Greater use of non-prescription medicines for minor ailments would flow from an enhanced role for the community pharmacy, according to the Irish Pharmaceutical Healthcare Association. The Association proposes that savings of £60m per annum could be made if people were encouraged to take more personal responsibility for everyday aches and pains, seeking the advice of the pharmacist where appropriate.

Complementary medicine

Two core issues are raised in submissions in respect of complementary medicine and complementary therapies:

• The need for greater access and choice of complementary medicine

• Regulation of medicines and registration of therapists.

These developments are supported by several groups and organisations involved in the field of complementary medicine, for example, the Acupuncture and Chinese Medicine Association, the Irish Association of Medical Herbalists and the Irish Society of Homeopaths.

The Irish Association of Health Stores makes the case for an important role for 'gentler forms of natural medicines, especially for everyday self-limiting conditions,' and argues that people should have free access to alternative systems of medicine, alongside appropriate forms of regulation.

There are proposals that GPs should have knowledge of local providers of complementary therapies and for all those involved in delivery of conventional medicine to have some training in the uses and potential of complementary medicine.

A number of women's groups and organisations see access to complementary medicine and therapy as an important strand in a strategy for women's health. The need for a support structure to facilitate this access is also raised.

The issue of access for medical card holders to complementary therapies and therapists is also raised.

The case for regulation of complementary medicine and registration of those involved is made by the Irish Medicines Board and also by the Irish Association of Health Stores (IAHS). IAHS suggests that the main objective of regulation should be the assurance of public safety while also preserving freedom of choice.

Counselling

The need for access to community-based counselling services is raised in many submissions. Some link this need with access to complementary therapies as a non-medical option for dealing with health issues such as stress.

Many kinds of counselling needs are highlighted in various submissions. These include:

• Counselling on reproductive health and sexually transmitted diseases

• Counselling for all those who have a chronic illness

• Genetic counselling

• Counselling for women in prostitution who have experienced violence

• Counselling on stress and stress management

• Women's counselling services

• Bereavement counselling services (extended to friends and schools when a suicide occurs).

The organisation for young people with cancer, Canteen, talks about the importance of counselling for the members of that organisation:

> People have needs outside being exposed to treatments that treat tumours. Cancer patients must also
> address issues involved in living with cancer. The emotional and lifestyle changes are huge in some

circumstances, for people living with cancer. Cancer patients really need their emotional needs
treated as well as their physical needs.

The Psychological Society of Ireland (PSI) suggests that provision of psychological support for people with severe health difficulties could yield great benefit, citing the fact that psychological factors are one of the strongest predictors of recovery from heart disease.

Comhar, the national counselling service for adults, recommends that counselling services should be delivered within local communities in locations that are non-stigmatising while also ensuring privacy. The organisation makes the case for systems of self-referral as a way of minimising barriers to access and enhancing motivation to attend. Research on counselling and psychotherapy outcomes reports more positive outcomes from self-referral, according to Comhar.

The availability of counselling for people with medical cards is raised as an access issue.

Health issues and needs of major population groups

People experiencing poverty and social exclusion

Many organisations (15 per cent) made proposals aimed at enhancing and improving the health and well-being of people experiencing poverty and social exclusion. Several of these organisations made parallel submissions to the consultation process being undertaken by the National Anti-Poverty Strategy (NAPS) for the purpose of setting targets for the revised NAPS.

The outcome of the NAPS Consultation Process has been the subject of a detailed report, which has fed directly into the process of preparing the Health Strategy. A summary of that report prepared by the Institute of Public Health is presented in Part 5. In the interests of avoiding undue overlap, this topic is not also covered in this section of the report.

The health of children and young people

The Council for Children's Hospitals' Care makes a general point about the strategic importance of a focus on children's health:

Child health is a key area requiring attention if the general standard of health of the population
and inequalities in health are to be satisfactorily addressed. The potential to achieve significant
health gain from preventative measures and interventions among children necessitates a high
priority being attached to this area. Improvement in the health status of children has the potential
to act as a foundation through which lasting gains in total population health can be realised.

In terms of strategic development, the Children's Rights Alliance sees the *Best Health for Children Programme* as an appropriate strategy for children from birth to twelve years. It welcomes the commitment to this programme, contained in the National Children's Strategy and recommends speedy implementation.

The National Youth Council focuses strongly on the needs of young people who are marginalised and socially excluded. The Council notes several important strategies and reports that make recommendations for young people's health and endorses their proposals. The strategy for adolescent health produced by the Conjoint Health Committee *Get Connected – Developing an Adolescent Friendly Health Service* is seen as a key to adolescent health and the development of an adolescent-friendly health service.

The Council sees a need for effective mechanisms to co-ordinate and implement these strategies and wants to see an interdepartmental, cross-sectoral structure put in place, which is tasked with the responsibility for this co-ordination. The Community and Voluntary Sector should be participants in monitoring and evaluating progress.

In its submission, Barnardos expresses serious concern about deficits in children's primary healthcare services, particularly with regard to assessments for a range of sensory and other difficulties:

> *Throughout our consultation with parents, the issues of long delays in having children assessed in relation to speech, language and hearing concerns was consistently cited as a serious concern. Many children are on waiting lists for assessment for many months. When they finally get an assessment or diagnosis, they are then transferred to further waiting lists for treatment services, often for up to or beyond a year. In effect, this means that children's needs are not being met during some of their most critical developmental periods.*

The organisation proposes that a comprehensive range of screening, developmental checks, primary healthcare, speech, language, dental and psychological services should be available and accessible to all within their local community.

The Faculty of Paediatrics of the Royal College of Physicians of Ireland proposes the need for enhanced community paediatrics through the appointment of consultant paediatricians with a special interest in community child health.

With regard to early years care and education, Barnardos proposes a wide range of specific changes to the Child Care Act, 1991 and the Pre-School Regulations, 1996.

Family support services

Flexible out-of-hours support services are needed by families, according to submissions. Barnardos proposes that community-based family support initiatives be established in each community care area with the following elements:

- Service user consultation systems

- Interagency working protocols

- Validated evaluation systems

- Programmes for vulnerable families that are integrated into mainstream programmes

- Extension of the family support worker and home-help schemes.

The development of parenting education programmes, suited to the ages and stages of children's development is also recommended in submissions.

Women's health services

Several submissions deal specifically with women's health issues and women's health services. At a strategic level, the following points are made:

- The commitments made in the 1997 Plan for Women's Health should be fulfilled, as an integral part of the Health Strategy

- The forthcoming Review of the Plan for Women's Health, currently being conducted on behalf of the Women's Health Council, should be taken into account

- The Health Strategy should be gender-proofed.

Men's health

The only submission to deal in detail with men's health was the submission from AMEN, the support organisation for male victims of domestic violence. The organisation believes that a far higher priority is given to women's health than to men's health. The submission acknowledges the beginnings of progress to address this situation but sees a need for much more to be done.

Workers' health

A small number of submissions address the question of the health of workers in general.

The Faculty of Occupational Medicine of the Royal College of Physicians argues that effective protection of the workforce is part of health and safety management and cannot be addressed through general lifestyle health promotion. The group makes a series of recommendations for occupational health and the role of the occupational health physician. The overall recommendation is for the development of an occupational health service for Ireland, based on the system in operation in Finland, which is generally recognised internationally for its quality and effectiveness.

Mobile units visiting workplaces are recommended by the Occupational Health Nurses Association of Ireland.

Victims of abuse

A number of submissions call for improved services for victims of abuse. Children, women and men who are victims of domestic violence all need enhanced protection as well as improved support services.

The Dublin Rape Crisis Centre makes the case for the streamlining of services for victims of sexual violence in Dublin and enhancement of the resources for the proposed National Referral Helpline.

Linkages and connections

The need for more effective linkages and connections within and between service providers, so as to offer the service user a seamless service and reduce fragmented service delivery was a theme in many submissions.

The contributions vary in their emphasis. Some highlight the need for inter-professional linkages and the sharing of information among professionals. Others go further to propose multidisciplinary working and team focused work. Views as to the composition of teams vary depending on the perspective of the contributor. The central importance of community involvement is stressed.

There were calls for closer linkages among providers working in community-based service delivery and proposals for structured connections between levels of service, for example, between GP services, hospital services and nursing homes.

Some contributions recognise the complexity of developing linkages among professionals and services – the issues of role definition, shared understandings of role, complex issues of power and position. For example:

> Focus needs to be placed on promoting and facilitating the delivery of healthcare through inter-professional partnership for the benefit of the patient. For a partnership model to be effective, the old hierarchical thinking in relation to the professions must disappear, along with the turf wars which are a barrier to patient care. (Pharmaceutical Society of Ireland)

And in a similar vein:

> …there must be a shared objective of providing a quality, flexible, accessible and accountable service accompanied by co-operation and flexibility by all players. To be really effective, there must also be co-operation and understanding of the respective roles among all healthcare workers at a local level so that the primary focus can be maintained on the health needs of the community rather than the self-interests of individual players.

The following listing describes several of the practical proposals from various professional groupings as to how linkages could be promoted:

- Mechanisms and protocols for interprofessional interaction

- An alternative structure for the provision of government funding, moving from a system whereby individual professional activities (for example, items prescribed or dispensed) are remunerated, to one that measures patient care

- As more GPs acquire special clinical skills, health boards, private health insurers and the GMS should support inter-referral

- The role of the public health nurse as caseload manager should be developed, with responsibility for registered nurses and for co-ordinating inputs from the specialist branches of the nursing profession

- A system of client tracking between primary and secondary care sectors to allow efficient management of care and comprehensive service delivery

- GPs should be able to link into hospital consultant files

- Consultants should have access to GPs computer files

- Information technology should be utilised to provide island people with linkages between mainland services and island nurses

- The National Cardiovascular Strategy as an example of an effective integrated approach

- Hospital staff to follow patients into community following discharge, where appropriate

- Structured referral and co-ordination systems between the health and social service providers dealing with children and families

- A case management approach to health service provision for children and families, especially those who are socially excluded.

Chapter 7

Meeting the health needs of older people

Introduction

The health needs of older people were raised in 15 per cent of submissions. These submissions came from both national and local community organisations, user groups, carer support groups, organisations and groups of professionals, service providers in both public and private sector and representative bodies.

The context is one of changing demographics and a significant growth in the proportion and numbers of older people in the population.

The major focus of submissions was on the need for a flexible range of supports to enable older people to stay in their homes and in their own communities for as long as possible.

Support for the concept of a continuum of support and care options, facilitating choice both through a comprehensive range of support services and through the manner of their delivery and funding, is evident in the submissions.

As part of the theme of community-based services, the need for supports for family-based carers is also raised in several submissions.

The main themes raised in submissions were the following:

- Broad principles and strategic proposals for supporting older people's health

- Community services

- Support for carers

- Assessment and rehabilitation

- Residential services.

Hospital services and the needs of particular groups of older people were also discussed in a number of submissions.

Broad principles and strategic proposals

While much of the material in submissions identified needs for specific services, some also offered principles and broad frameworks for service planning and delivery.

Several principles to underpin approaches to meeting the needs of older people are suggested. These include:

• Promoting respect for older people

• Positive acknowledgement of older people, their experiences, skills, past and present contributions

• Promotion and facilitation of independence and autonomy

• Elimination of ageism.

Some more specific operational principles and strategic approaches are also mentioned:

• Need for a cross-cutting approach to policy

• Delivering a 'seamless service'

• Community-focused, responsive and flexible services

• High standards and quality of service at all levels

• Recognition and valuing of the role of informal care

• A 'whole person' approach.

The need for an integrated approach to provision is emphasised. Detailed research on the linkages between health status and standards of living of older people is described by the National Council on Ageing and Older People, who underline the need for a co-ordinated and integrated strategy which provides for funding for health, housing and support services, as well as dealing with all other determinants of health.

Matrons/Nurse Managers in Elderly Care Services in a health board make the case for establishing a new infrastructure to deliver a seamless service to the older person:

> A single point of contact [is needed] with devolved budgeting, budgets shared between the health, social service and other statutory bodies...We strongly recommend the provision of a case manager, who will ultimately be responsible and accountable for services required by the person and who will advocate on his or her behalf.

The National Council on Ageing and Older People recommends the introduction of a concept of "care management" for older people, as a model to co-ordinate services for older people. "Care management" involves developing packages of care for dependent older people...tailored to their individual needs'.

The Council also recommends the provision of a framework of designated core services, with statutory underpinning. The implications of such a policy are described as follows:

> This designation would require the State to provide the services to all who need them on the grounds of dependency or social circumstances. Clear and Universal Guidelines for the assessment of eligibility on the basis of need would be established at a national level. The discretionary nature of the services would be replaced by a transparent and equitable system of service delivery. The services should be underpinned by legislation and appropriate funding.

The Association of Health Boards proposes similar strategic change in the way resources are given to older people:

> With a view to ensuring that elderly people will be able to live in their own communities to the maximum extent the equivalent of the nursing home subvention should be payable to the elderly person to enable them to arrange a package of care in their own homes.

On the point of a 'whole person' approach, the following comment from Age and Opportunity exemplifies the concern:

> Medical and care needs do come first, but we all at any age have a continuing need to have some sense of control over our lives, even when we have become frail. It is essential to our well-being in any setting that we have some choice and privacy, as well as opportunities to become involved in meaningful activities. Very little or no recreational opportunities are provided in care settings. Neglect of people's need for stimulation and meaningful involvement in a variety of activities can, in our view, amount to abuse of older people.

Community services

The need for community-based services, to help older people to remain at home or in their community for as long as they wish attracts a high level of attention in submissions.

Health promotion/community participation

While many contributors focus on care and treatment services, several also highlight the potential of health promotion geared to the needs of older people and the need to provide opportunities for autonomy, community participation and recreation. Age and Opportunity points to several successful music, drama and visual arts projects, for example those run in partnership with Midland Health Board, Laois County Council Arts Office and the organisation Music Network. Age and Opportunity makes a recommendation on this matter:

> That the Health Strategy include a commitment to co-operate with the providers of a range of social and cultural services – in areas like education, the arts, public libraries and leisure to ensure that their services are inclusive of older people and targeted at them.

There is a proposal from Knocknacarra Active Retirement Association that funding would be given to local groups to help them to engage professionals to provide group physiotherapy, reflexology, PE, as a cost-effective means of involving older people together in health promoting activities.

The importance of involving older people themselves in the planning of activities and services in their communities is raised in submissions.

Community care

There are calls for a wide range of community-based care, support and treatment facilities for older people and increased numbers of health professionals.

Among the most frequently mentioned services are the following:

- Day centres/day care facilities

- Home help services

- Night sitters

- Domiciliary nursing

- Laundry services

- Visiting personnel – public health nurses, GPs, physiotherapists, occupational therapists, chiropodists, social workers

- Respite service, both in the home and outside the home

- Opportunities for shared care between family and residential services

- Meals-on-wheels and lunch clubs

- Services of a dietician

- Easier access to technical and mechanical aids and appliances and home modifications

- Day hospitals

- Transport to community-based health and social services

- Social housing/group homes

- A social visiting service.

Summerhill Active Retirement Group suggests that many of these services might be delivered through 'Third Age Centres' as part of an overall 'active ageing' strategy, in conjunction with health promotion.

Support for carers

Closely linked to the need for improved community services is the need for more support for family members caring for older people. A specific concern is raised about people caring for those with particular conditions such as strokes and the need for therapist help with regard to feeding, speaking and toileting.

The case is made in submissions for a greater recognition of the place and value of informal, family caring and for more comprehensive supports for carers.

One of the issues arising here also is the argument for a non means-tested carer's allowance, which would be a statutory entitlement for all full time carers. Informal caring is competing with employment schemes such as back-to-work schemes that are more financially rewarding.

Workplace day care centres for older people have been successful in the US, according to the Irish Society of Physicians in Geriatric Medicine.

While the value of family care is generally acknowledged, a caution and caveat is raised by the National Council on Ageing and Older People, to the effect that not all older people may wish to depend on family caring and many families may not be in a position to give adequate care.

Assessment and rehabilitation

Access to assessment and rehabilitation services is seen as an essential ingredient of the care and support strategy, though there are differences of view as to whether rehabilitation services should be separate from acute services, or located on acute hospital sites.

The provision of assessment services must be coherent with means testing arrangements, according to a group of Matrons/Nurse Managers in Elderly Care Services:

> The opportunity for rehabilitation must be included as an integral and initial part of any care assessment before any irreversible decisions on long-term care are taken. This requires that the concept of placement subvention means testing should not be undertaken within at least the first 2 to 3 months and the provision for this service must be available locally.

The issue of assessment mechanisms is also raised by the Irish Society of Physicians in Geriatric Medicine, who argue for a clear and fair assessment system, where financial incentives are away from, rather than towards, long-term residential care:

> Currently, the only legislation [The Nursing Home Act] in this area acts as an incentive if anything towards long-term care...Within nursing homes, patients side by side may have a 'contract bed' or may be paying for it themselves. There is no clear financial pathway to decide what applies to a given patient.

Long-term residential care

The main proposals made in respect of long-term residential care are the following:

*   More health board facilities for long-term care

*   More affordable facilities

*   Facilities close to people's homes

*   Need for unannounced inspections, at varying times, in public and private facilities.

The National Council on Ageing and Older People emphasises the issue of quality in long-term care and signals its concern at the lack of development of uniform standards in all long-term residential care facilities. The Council draws attention to its own report, *Framework for Quality in Long-Term Residential Care for Older People in Ireland 2000*. The establishment of a representative working group on quality assurance in long-term residential care is advocated.

The Alzheimer Society proposes that the cost of long-term care should be addressed and that national disparities in those costs be examined. The Society wants a standard method of calculating the nursing home subvention, with calculations available to the applicant for examination.

Acute care

The high level of usage of acute services by older people, relative to their proportion of the population is raised by the Irish Society of Physicians in Geriatric Medicine. The Society goes on to make a series of detailed recommendations about the quantity and management of acute care and provision of out-patient care. One of the main proposals is that admissions of those over seventy years should be under the care of a geriatrician with an associated team, unless a person suffers from a single specific illness which would be more effectively treated under another specialty.

In respect of day hospital/out-patient care, the Society proposes a rapid ambulatory assessment and diagnostic facility/day hospital, which would respond speedily to referrals and would be located on each acute hospital site. Among the range of specialist clinics provided would be:

- Osteoporosis treatment and fracture prevention clinic

- Memory clinic

- Parkinson's disease clinic

- Continence promotion.

Older people with special needs

The specialised needs of people with dementia are raised in a number of submissions. It should be noted that the Alzheimer Society believes that services for people with Alzheimer's disease and related dementias should be taken from under the umbrella of services for older people and should be addressed as a unique client group.

The National Council on Ageing and Older People draws attention to its action plan for dementia care, which contains 33 costed targets, covering all aspects of the health needs of this group and proposes that these be integrated into the Health Strategy and the National Anti-Poverty Strategy. Similarly, the Alzheimer Society makes an extensive series of proposals, including rights-based service entitlements to service.

Another group of older people whose needs receive particular mention are those older people who live on the islands. Comdháil Oileáin na hÉireann proposes the need for a plan for older people on the islands, which would include high dependency unit, respite, daycare, home support services and transport.

Chapter 8

Meeting the needs of people with disabilities

Introduction

Submissions make a wide range of proposals regarding meeting the needs of people with disabilities. This chapter sets our proposals from organisations for meeting the needs of:

8.1 People with mental health difficulties

8.2 People with physical and sensory disabilities and chronic illnesses or conditions

8.3 People with learning difficulties

8.1 **People with mental health difficulties**

Introduction

Proposals concerning mental health needs were made in approximately 13 per cent of submissions. The submissions commented on legislation, policy, strategic development, funding, the need for changes in service delivery systems and improved practice in supporting people with mental health difficulties.

Legislation and policy

The Department of Health and Children is urged to ensure speedy implementation of the new Mental Health Act. The delay in implementation is a cause of concern. The Royal College of Psychiatrists proposes a number of amendments to the Act.

At policy level, there are some calls for *Planning for the Future* to be updated, or replaced with a new mental health strategy, but it is also suggested that much of the focus of that Report remains valid and needs to be implemented. There is recognition of improved investment in the sector in recent years 'albeit on a modest scale compared with other health sectors'. (Mental Health Association of Ireland)

The Cluain Mhuire Service Management Team, St. John of God Brothers, is critical of the policy and model of sectorisation. It sees this approach to service delivery as incompatible with a patient-focused service. While it was originally intended as a way of ensuring continuity of care during de-institutionalisation of large mental hospitals, the Cluain Mhuire submission states that its impact is to deny choice to public patients as to where they present for assessment, care and treatment. This is a view which is strongly supported by the Simon Community, in relation to services for homeless people.

The National Disability Authority (NDA) proposes that a new mental health strategy is required, which would include sectoral plans based on a national needs assessment.

Funding and service delivery

In relation to funding, further investment in capital funding, over and above that provided for in the National Development Plan is thought by the Mental Health Association of Ireland (MHAI) to be needed in order to provide a modern and comprehensive mental health service.

The need for equity of funding with other disability areas is raised:

> As many of the users of mental health services are from the more deprived and marginalised areas of society, the onus for ensuring that they get equity within the system falls heavily on the decision makers within the system…To date the mental health services have suffered from underfunding and this must be addressed within the Strategy. (Royal College of Psychiatrists)

The main aspects of service delivery that are the focus of attention were:

- Community-based mental health services

- Special mental health issues for particular groups

- Quality of care and approaches to addressing mental illness.

Linkages between services and among service providers are also discussed, as well as acute care and residential care.

Community-based services

The centrality of a holistic approach to mental health issues, which addresses employment and accommodation as well as treatment and care services, is underlined in submissions.

Several contributors express serious concern at what they see as the failure to integrate mental healthcare into the primary care system and the poor linkages between community and hospital care.

The Aware organisation calls for a fundamental review of the difficulties encountered in the management of people with psychiatric problems by GPs and the problems of continuity of care.

Gaps in the provision of consultant-led multi-disciplinary teams are seen as another structural difficulty in service provision at community level. This is partly on account of recruitment difficulties in relation to psychologists, social workers and occupational therapists who would link with community psychiatric nurses and consultant psychiatrists.

The Health and Social Services Working Group of Fingal Development Board proposes improvements in the infrastructure for service delivery, including the creation of a community health professional post, with specific expertise in supporting people with mental health difficulties.

A further structure proposed by Aware is the provision of advocacy services for those with mental health problems and the appointment of an Ombudsman especially for the mental health services.

There are many proposals for improvements in the levels of service 'on the ground'. The main concerns are for developments in relation to:

- Community nursing

- Day centres and drop-in centres

- Family support, respite care, home carers

- Specialist fostering

- Telephone helpline service

- Public awareness campaigns

- Improved allowances in workshops

- Improved transport for workshop services

- Supported accommodation.

There are also calls for greater flexibility and out-of-hours provision of services.

Special mental health issues for particular groups

In a small number of submissions, attention is drawn to the particular mental health needs of certain groups. New developments in relation to mental health services for adolescents and for older people are seen as very positive, but much more is needed. Positive developments need to be standardised around the country, according to the Psychiatric Nurses Association of Ireland. Improvements are also needed, it is argued, in mental health services for people with learning disabilities, rehabilitation services and acute psychiatric treatment services.

As well as essential developments in sub-specialties, the Royal College of Psychiatrists wants to see improved interfaces between child and adolescent psychiatry and adult psychiatry and increasing access to allied healthcare professionals.

Child and adolescent mental health services

Improvements needed in child and adolescent psychiatric services include the following:

- Rural services

- Specialised counselling

- Locally-based assessment

- Provision for self-referral

- Telephone helplines

- Bereavement counselling.

Older people

The Royal College of Psychiatrists welcomes the recruitment of consultants for old age psychiatry but the needs of a patient with pre-senile dementia and those with long histories of mental health problems need to be addressed.

Dealing with eating disorders

The services for people who have eating disorders are of special concern to Bodywhys, the organisation offering support and help for people with anorexia and bulimia nervosa. Citing 1998 statistics for hospital admissions for people with eating disorders, the organisation points to research which found only three publicly funded hospital beds specifically for eating disorders for the whole country, located in Dublin. Most private provision is also located in Dublin.

Bodywhys proposes a coherent national policy for addressing eating disorders, including local counselling and psychotherapy, family therapy, training for health professionals and families, more dedicated services, dietary advice, a treatment centre and research.

Suicide prevention

Concern about levels of suicide is raised in several submissions. The National Suicide Review Group points out that Ireland has one of the fastest rising suicide rates in the world, with suicide being the leading cause of death among young Irish people and the male rate of suicide having risen by 400 per cent in the past 20 years. The Review Group acknowledges that suicide is 'on the agenda' now and makes the case for 'a coherent, integrated and well-planned national strategy for suicide prevention'.

The Group recommends that the Department of Health and Children should endorse and support the work of developing a National Suicide Prevention Action Plan, following on from the work of the Task Force on Suicide. A further recommendation is that the Department would endorse proposals made by the Group to health board CEOs for the establishment in each health board of a permanent post of suicide resource officer, with a standardised role.

The mental health needs of homeless people

Simon Community raises a number of concerns, including the lack of accommodation for those who are mentally ill. According to Simon, the policy of 'sectorisation', introduced following the publication of *Planning for the Future*, meets the needs of the settled population but is unsuited to homeless people. The policy requires that 'a person's access to psychiatric services is based on where the person originally came from rather than where they are living now.'

Simon makes a series of recommendations for improved mental health services for people with mental health problems who are homeless. The first of these is that for the purpose of service provision, people should have their mental illness treated as their primary condition. Others deal with needs assessment, accommodation, implementation of good practice guidelines and a statutory right to mental health services.

The mental health needs of prisoners

Several contributors draw attention to the needs of prisoners with mental health difficulties. They draw attention to the recent report from the Irish Penal Reform Trust and make the case for a high priority to be given to improving psychiatric services and other mental health services for prisoners.

Quality of care and approaches to mental healthcare

Many contributors make proposals concerning the quality of care. The main recommendations cover the following aspects of care:

- Greater use of counselling and alternative therapies and less reliance on medication

- A wider skills mix on multi-disciplinary teams

- Retaining people in acute care for as long as they need to be there

- Aftercare programmes, structured preparation for discharge from hospital

- More time with doctor/consultant on individual visits

- Training for health professionals in relation to mental health and mental illness, including training for working with people with eating disorders

- Intensive training for GPs in relation to mental health/mental illness

- Access to high quality activities in day and residential centres.

At an infrastructural level, there are several proposals for the development of regulations, standards and codes of practice for mental health services, which should be the subject of audit and reporting.

The provision of a system of advocacy services is also recommended (at the minimum this should meet the PPF commitment to provide advocacy services to people detained under the Mental Health Act).

8.2 Meeting the needs of people with physical and sensory disabilities and chronic illnesses or conditions

Introduction

The needs of people with physical and sensory disabilities and chronic conditions are addressed in 10 per cent of submissions, which came from local disability groups, national advocacy or support organisations and from national representative bodies. Not surprisingly, quite a number of the submissions deal in detail with the concerns of people with particular named conditions or disabilities. The broad thrust of these submissions will be reflected here, but it would not be possible to cover the detailed recommendations from each group.

The material in submissions covers the following:

• Policy frameworks

• Community services

• Needs of particular groups

• Quality systems.

Policy frameworks

The thrust of the submissions reflects the move towards a rights-based, social model of disability, with emphasis on access (in the broadest sense of that term), inclusion, choice and independence.

The particular social context within which the needs of people with physical disabilities are to be met is a complex one, offering both opportunities and challenges. The Disability Federation of Ireland (DFI) sees the move to mainstream service provision, changing family structures, new technology and increased levels of self-determination and personal responsibility among people with disabilities as important influences on future policy.

A number of national and international agreements and reports are cited as offering the appropriate policy frameworks for a strategy for health services for people with disabilities. These include the UN Standard Rules, The Maastricht Treaty (Article 13A) and the Report of the Commission on the Status of People with Disabilities.

The National Disability Authority (NDA) makes the case for a legal framework for health and disability services which would include a statement of rights, underpinning principles, key objectives for healthcare and disability support services, accountability structures and provision for monitoring and evaluation at all levels. The Authority also proposes that the Health Strategy should be disability-proofed.

The Post-Polio Support Group is concerned that the non-inclusion of disabled citizens over the age of sixty-five years in the Department of Health and Children's Physical and Sensory Database results in problems for those in the age group sixty-five to seventy, who are disabled but living independently. They cannot qualify for a medical card until the age of seventy and are excluded as a result from many disability benefits such as access to aids and appliances.

Community services

The continued development of community-based services is a theme running through the submissions concerning the needs of people with physical disabilities.

There are proposals for a new infrastructure for service delivery, which include a national assessment and support process, with a statutory underpinning. The thrust of the proposals is well captured in this proposal from the Families and Friends Association of Scoil Mochua:

> *Each person with a physical/mental disability [should] be assessed and an individual statement of needs drawn up with regard to therapy, education and all necessary supports. The implementation of same should be a statutory entitlement. Based on that assessment of needs, the money should then be 'tied' to the individual.*

Similarly, the NDA proposes an assessment process, independent of service provision, together with the development of 'support co-ordination' to advise people on the range of services available and actively assist them to access those services.

A wide range of very varied proposals for enhanced levels of service were named including:

- Parent and family support, flexibly geared to the times people need them

- Activity-based respite

- Accessible transport

- Access to the services of a dietician

- Funding for personal assistance that is ringfenced at health board level for that purpose

- Home-based occupational therapy

- Access to counselling, physiotherapy, hydrotherapy

- Mainstream equality training

- Full implementation of the 3 per cent employment quota in the public service

- Safety harnesses on school transport and bus escorts

- Aids and appliances

- Prohibition on loading on insurance on the basis of a diagnosis of a genetically determined condition

- Funding for special schools for wheelchairs, hoists, aids and appliances.

Funding and income support

The question of the cost of disability is raised by PwDI, which details the case for recognition of the additional costs for individuals as a result of disability. The organisation proposes the setting up of a consultative forum to examine this matter, in conjunction with the National Anti-Poverty Strategy.

Eastern Vocational Enterprises Limited (Eve Holdings) draws attention to commitments in the PPF to the setting up of an inter-departmental working group to examine the feasibility of a costs of disability payment.

The Meath Centre for Independent Living proposes direct payments to people with disabilities, so that they can choose their own service providers.

There is a proposal that the mobility allowance should not be means-tested and a further proposal that the motorised transport grant should be available to passengers with disabilities.

Meeting the needs of particular groups

Several submissions put forward wide-ranging strategies for addressing the needs of people who have particular disabilities or conditions. A brief overview of some concerns and recommendations is given here to highlight the range of proposals. It is worth emphasising again that all of the submissions and proposals have been fed into the various groups working on the development of the Health Strategy.

Children with disabilities

In its submission, the Children's Rights Alliance (CRA) draws attention to the Concluding Observations of the UN Committee on the Rights of the Child, where the Committee expressed its concern at the lack of a national policy to ensure the rights of children with disabilities and recommended that, in the light of Article 23 of the Convention on the rights of the Child, the Government should develop programmes to facilitate their active participation in the community.

PwDI proposes the establishment of an independent assessment and support process for children in each health board. The issue of close interdepartmental working, as a prerequisite for effective service delivery to children, is also raised in this and in other submissions.

People with head injury/spinal injury

Headway Ireland makes a series of proposals as to how services for people with head injury need to be configured, arising out of an understanding of the impact of brain injury on the life of the individual:

> Brain injury needs to be seen in terms of a chronic condition with lifelong consequences rather than an acute medical event that requires short-term rehabilitation followed by a return to normal functioning for the individual. The long-term consequences of brain injury for social integration, a return to work and interpersonal relationships have been highlighted in previous research and any model of brain injury services needs to be based on such a long-term view of the condition.

The organisation proposes the setting up of a working group to contribute to the development of a national strategy on brain injury, similar to those in place for heart disease, alcoholism and drugs.

The National Rehabilitation Hospital in Dublin also proposes a wide-ranging and in-depth strategy for the treatment, care, rehabilitation and inclusion of people in need of medical rehabilitation.

A case management/advocacy structure should be part of the service, together with specialist assessment and nursing in a location appropriate to needs. Protocols for the treatment and care of people with head injury should be adopted by health boards. Improved data for planning purposes needs to be collected by health boards.

The overarching proposal is for the establishment of a broad-based consultative group representing all key services and client groups to develop, plan and monitor a national medical rehabilitation strategy and programme for the whole of Ireland.

People with sensory disabilities

The National Association for the Deaf (NAD) makes the case for priority to be given to the development of the sensory sector and additional resources to enable it to catch up on other sectors.

The Association makes a proposal for access to mainstream health services for deaf people in their own locality using videophone technology to provide remote sign language interpretation at the point of contact between deaf service users and health service providers.

A number of local and regionally-based groups and organisations call for a range of improvements in services for people with sensory disabilities. The improvements sought include:

*   Improved access to interpreter services for deaf people in their areas

*   Improved physical access in hospitals for blind people

*   Better physical access in local communities.

People with chronic conditions

Several support groups make the case for strategies for people with particular conditions, including people suffering from diabetes, lupus, sleep apnoea, fibromyalgia, ME, stoma, coeliac disease, incontinence, neurofibromatosis, Hepatitis C/Anti-D, lymphodoema and tinnitus.

All of the groups make detailed proposals as to how to address the needs of the people supported by their organisation or profession. They propose that research be undertaken in respect of the health problems with which they are concerned. They also propose staff awareness training in relation to the health issues of disabilities groups with which they are working. Some examples of the proposals are given here.

The Diabetes Federation offers a detailed account of its experience of the limitations in hospital and community services for people with diabetes, problems arising from poor detection and what it sees as a low priority for diabetes from a public health standpoint.

The Federation makes a comprehensive series of proposals for a national diabetes care strategy, involving improved detection services, shared diabetes care between hospital and GP, regional and national registers, research, utilisation of new technological developments in both treatment and in data collection and data sharing methodologies.

The Lymphodoema Support Group wants to see the establishment of a lymphodoema service. A further point raised is the need for the very high cost of special hosiery for lymphodoema sufferers (£700 per annum in one case) to be covered under the Drugs Payment Scheme.

The Cork Tinnitus Support Group proposes the establishment of at least one national clinic dedicated to therapeutic programmes for the relief and management of tinnitus.

8.3 **Meeting the needs of people with learning difficulties**

Introduction

The specific needs of people with learning difficulties were addressed in 7 per cent of submissions. The broad issues raised focus on equity of access to service, rights to service provision, income support and quality of service.

Equity and rights

Both the National Association for Mentally Handicapped in Ireland (NAMHI) and the National Federation of Voluntary Bodies providing Services to People with Mental Handicap argue the case for equitable access to service for people with learning difficulties.

NAMHI believes that legislation is essential to ensure such equity and looks forward to the proposed Disabilities Bill. The organisation proposes that the Health Strategy must underwrite and subscribe to that Bill. NAMHI also proposes that the recommendations of the Commission on the Status of People with Disabilities should form the basis of recommendations in the Health Strategy.

NAMHI argues that disparities in levels of service, as well as services in unsuitable and inappropriate settings, are a serious problem. According to NAMHI, these disparities have been confirmed in a recent report from the Health Research Board and in the annual reports from the Inspector of Mental Hospitals.

The Hospitaller Order of St. John of God raises the issue of access to primary health services for people with a disability in general and for people with a learning disability in particular. One example given is that of access to mainstream psychiatric services:

> *Often people with an intellectual disability are denied access to appropriate mental health services*
> — *on the excuse that the generic psychiatric services do not have the resources or the responsibility. This issue needs resolution in the context of the Government's Health Strategy.*

The submission from St. Joseph's Association for the Mentally Handicapped, Portrane, makes a particular case for equity of provision for people with learning disabilities within psychiatric services and in Portrane in particular.

Demand for access for people with learning disabilities to medical interventions such as transplants is made by the Inishowen Learning Disability Network who also makes the case for a statutory entitlement to therapy services and aids and appliances.

The equity issue is raised in relation to people with learning difficulties who have additional needs. The Order of St. John of God is very concerned about the need for a policy and service for people with challenging behaviour, as well as for people with a dual diagnosis of intellectual disability and mental illness. The Order is concerned at what it sees as a total lack of appropriate services for people with such a dual diagnosis. The problem should get priority in health service planning, it is argued.

Income support

Levels of poverty among people with learning disabilities and concerns about income support are highlighted by the National Federation of Voluntary Bodies providing Services to People with Mental Handicap and by PwDI. The Federation makes a series of proposals about income support and accommodation:

> *People with intellectual disability are among the poorest in our society. Those in institutionalised care do not receive disability allowance – they have no tenancy rights in their homes and often live in overcrowded conditions, sharing bedrooms and have few day activities.*

According to the Federation, the Health Strategy needs to be proactive about advocating for a disability allowance for all people with learning disabilities including those in large centres and about securing tenancy rights.

Quality of service

National standards applicable to all services for people with a learning disability and a mental illness are proposed as a matter of urgency, together with the licensing of services and the development of a national accreditation system.

At an operational level the case is made in several submissions for improvements in career guidance, home-school liaison, respite and residential services, access to all therapies, support for carers and retirement homes.

A range of special provisions to meet the specific needs of people with autism is put forward by Hope, a support organisation for families of children with autism. Hope proposes the setting up of a specialist integrated healthcare clinic/research centre for persons suffering from autistic spectrum disorders and related biologies.

Chapter 9

The infrastructure of the health system

Introduction

Many submissions (32 per cent) discuss broad policy perspectives, principles, planning, research and administrative structures.

The main themes covered here are:

- The broad determinants of health and the case for a systemic approach to health policy and planning

- Principles to underpin the new Health Strategy

- Research and planning

- The voluntary/statutory interface

- Administrative structures

- Legislation

- Implementing and monitoring the Strategy.

The broad determinants of health

Contributors highlight the linkages between the health of individuals and communities and all aspects of people's lives. The holistic nature of health and well-being calls for a broadly-based and integrated policy response to the challenge of optimising the health of the nation, according to the contributors.

The need for this approach is highlighted most strongly in the material concerning the health status of marginalised and disadvantaged communities and in respect of groups of the population who have special needs.

Strong connections are made between health status and the equality agenda, as is summed up in the following observation from Community Workers Co-Operative:

Improved access to healthcare on its own will not produce good health outcomes. There is a need to locate the discussion in the broader economic and social exclusion context. This requires an approach that integrates health objectives across a range of other policy arenas, i.e. accommodation, education, income adequacy, employment policy.

The Royal College of Physicians points to examples of poorly integrated past planning and looks to the Department of Health and Children to advocate for a new health-focused perspective in public policy-making:

The planning problems that have beset the country over the past decades are having an impact on well-being now. Examples include poor facilities such as children's playgrounds and recreational spaces in deprived areas, inadequate transport infrastructure and poorly regulated environmental monitoring. This has led to an unfortunate level of cynicism targeted at public authorities. The new Strategy offers a chance to redress this by clearly stating that the Government values the health of the population and that the Department of Health and Children is prepared to advocate so that health and social issues are given the prominence that is currently afforded to economic factors when public policy is being formulated.

Tools for integrated policy and planning

Practical tools are needed to deliver 'joined-up' policy and planning. At governmental level, the need for health proofing of social policy and the development of health impact assessment systems are proposed in several submissions. For example:

There must be integration of the health agenda within government, across government departments and with others in the statutory and non-statutory sectors. Health impact assessment must be considered to assess the impact on health of a range of policy measures and interventions. The development of a set of robust, easily measurable performance indicators for health impact across sectors should be developed. (Institute of Public Health)

And:

It is recommended that such health impact assessments be co-ordinated on a national basis by the Department of Health and Children (or a commissioned agency). This should be further supported by the external auditing of national and local organisations to assess whether and how child and youth health has been included in their policy development. (National Youth Council)

The National Youth Council also makes a case for the integration of all the separate strategies being developed or recently developed, for example for youth health, adolescent mental health and children's health so as to ensure that they cohere into a single overarching health strategy.

Arising out of this concern for a holistic approach to health, there are many calls for the setting up of mechanisms and structures to ensure effective interdepartmental, interagency and multi-disciplinary working, at national, regional and local levels. For example:

Closer co-operation is required between all government departments in developing an overall Strategy for our ageing society. Effective health and social services can only be achieved through close co-operation with other services, notably income maintenance... (Age Action Ireland)

As well as cross-sectoral working, the benefits that could accrue from cross-border co-operation are highlighted.

Principles to underpin the Strategy

Many contributors endorse the principles which underpinned the 1994 Health Strategy *Shaping a Healthier Future,* namely the principles of equity, quality of service and accountability. Several contributors put forward other principles which they would wish to see incorporated in the new Strategy. Among those proposed are the following:

- The principle of a rights-based, empowerment approach

- The principle of a holistic, social model of health

- A community development approach

- Care as the dominant value

- Flexibility

- Responsiveness to need

- The principle of respect for service users

- Principles of participation and consultation.

The Community and Voluntary Pillar, among other organisations, proposes the application of a 'rights-based' approach' to health. The Pillar develops that concept and its implications:

> *The Community and Voluntary Pillar considers access to essential health services as a basic human right and supports the campaign to have the right to healthcare inserted into the Constitution. Article 12 of the UN International Covenant on Economic, Social and Cultural Rights – to which Ireland is a signatory – sets out everyone's right to the enjoyment of the highest attainable standard of physical and mental health.*

> *The Community and Voluntary Pillar acknowledges that a rights-based approach to health and healthcare has implications for resource allocation but does not believe that health related rights are any less fundamental than civil and political rights.*

The Pillar also proposes a community development approach to health:

> *In this approach individuals become subjects, participants rather than objects of the exercise. The concern is with collective change in the health status and empowerment of the group as well as addressing the problems of individuals.*

> *The principles which inform community development have to do with participation; empowerment; choice; a belief in people's capacities to make rational decisions in the circumstances that face them; equality and a rights-based approach.*

Research and planning

An extensive research agenda emerges from the submissions. Some organisations raise issues around the research infrastructure and the strategic focus of research. Most identify specific research issues.

The Health Research Board outlines the potential strategic role for health research in promoting health, enhancing efficiency and effectiveness. Opportunities for health research can embed the healthcare industry in Ireland and can also 'hold' health professionals here for postgraduate training.

The Board proposes structures that would support a thriving research culture:

- Appointment of a research and development officer in the Department of Health and Children

- Appointment of research and development officers in health boards and in specialist health agencies

- Preparation by health boards and specialist agencies of research strategies reflecting health service priorities

- Establishment of a forum for health and social care to advise on research agendas.

Proposals for research

Proposals cover the conduct of specific research as well as data gathering for planning purposes.

The National Youth Council points to the lack of indicators for benchmarking policies and interventions to assist young people and makes a comprehensive series of recommendations for data collection to support planning of services for children and young people.

St. James's Hospital makes a case for explicit identification of the education/research expenditure/cost in the acute sector and an agreed basis for developing and funding this research. The submission also proposes that the boards of acute care agencies should be required 'to emphasise and promote the academic elements of their remits through significantly greater and explicit corporate focus than has been traditionally provided.'

The Department of Health Services Management, Trinity College, points to a dearth of research in the area of health service management and the need to provide the evidence base to guide initiatives. The Department sees a need to create a pool of established researchers in the area of health services research.

Most proposals dealt with the need to strengthen the research base of provision for particular groups or on specific health issues. Among those mentioned were:

- Prevention

- Research concerning service provision for older people

- Prevalence and responses to eating disorders

- Mental health research

- Dementia research

- True medical and pharmacological cost of asthma

- Research regarding the health needs of women

- The health needs and issues of women in prostitution

- Violence against men

- Suicide and suicide prevention

- Bereavement

- The needs, issues and concerns of people who are marginalised or deprived

- All areas of disability

- Research to support risk management, risk communication, informed consent and quality at all levels of the blood transfusion chain.

The voluntary/statutory interface

Thirteen percent (13 per cent) of organisations discuss the interface between the Community and Voluntary Sector and the State.

The White Paper on the relationship between the State and the Voluntary and Community Sector *Supporting Voluntary Activity* is referenced in several documents as providing the policy basis of the relationship. The commitments to partnership with the Community and Voluntary Sector in the 1994 Health Strategy are noted. These commitments place a high value on the role of the Voluntary and Community Sector.

The contribution of the sector is seen as very wide-ranging, going well beyond consultation to an engagement in mutually supportive endeavour. The submission from DFI highlights the range of voluntary sector activities in the field of disability:

> *Mobilising community support, identifier of needs, developer of responses, early response, flexible approach, provider of services, advocacy agent and builder of the capacity of people with disabilities and their families.*

It is notable that most of the contributions on this topic come from small local and community groups, who are working 'on the ground' in their communities and who want to enhance the role they play there.

Many organisations make mention of strong, supportive relationships with health boards which have served people well. Some have not had a positive experience and would like to see a more structured framework for supporting the work of voluntary groups. There is a proposal that health boards would employ a local co-ordinator who could advise groups regarding what the health board can do for them and how they can strengthen their contribution to their own local community.

In the main, these local organisations see great potential for working closely with statutory agencies for the benefit of many vulnerable groups. They want to have an equal role in identifying needs and have proactive support for their role. They wish to see active encouragement for support groups. These groups see a role for voluntary activity in the following areas:

- Social housing projects for people with mental health difficulties

- Home visiting with older people

- Youth services

- Cancer support

- Child care provision

- Respite provision

- Advocacy.

Resourcing for partnership is an issue for these groups. The Community Workers Co-Operative describes the resources needed to enable the sector to function well, saying that 'without resources and supports … the principle of participation will remain tokenistic and unproductive'.

The Diabetes Federation of Ireland recommends the setting up of a Voluntary Sector Unit within the Department of Health and Children, to provide support, facilitation and liaison with the Sector.

Other kinds of support mentioned are start-up grants for local groups and established criteria for funding similar to those used by the Department of Social, Community and Family Affairs.

Administrative structures

A small number of organisations raise issues concerning the present administrative structures and, in particular, the health board structures. There are some calls for re-organisation or restructuring, though few detailed proposals are provided.

The submission from St. James's Hospital suggests that regional structural arrangements are no longer appropriate to the requirements of a contemporary health system and that governance and management arrangements need to be modernised. Proposing the need for radical overhaul, St. James's Hospital considers that the following issues should be reviewed:

- Numbers, size and types of regions

- Shift from representational to expertise-based governance

- Separation of service procurement from service delivery

- Decentralisation of authority to agencies.

The Adelaide Hospital Society proposes four health authorities, a strong directly elected citizen voice and the establishment of a National Health Forum, with strong citizen and community representation, through which consensus on health priorities could be developed.

Legislation

The following were the main proposals for new legislation or adjustments to existing legislation:

- Legislation to ensure fundamental right to care in the community

- Legislative clarity about health and social service entitlements

- Consistency of legislative provision for long-term care

- Statutory rights to a package of core services

- Legislative underpinning for complaints and appeals procedures

- A new legal framework for disability services

- Amendments to the Child Care Act, 1991

- A new Pharmacy Act

- Review of the Dentists Act

- Search and reunion legislation in respect of people who have been adopted and their natural parents

- Reform of the Medical Practitioners Act, 1978

- Amendments to the Mental Health Act.

Implementing and monitoring the Strategy

Several contributors discuss ways of monitoring and implementing the Health Strategy. There are some references to the absence of monitoring processes in relation to the 1994 Strategy, *Shaping a Healthier Future*.

Among the proposals made are the following:

• Short-term and long-term targets are essential to both implementation and monitoring processes

• The views of users, their families and the wider community should be gathered on an ongoing basis and built into the ongoing monitoring and implementation arrangements

• Voluntary and community organisations should be involved in the monitoring process

• ESRI should be commissioned to monitor the Strategy

• A National Health Council comprising all stakeholders including representatives of consumers should be set up as part of monitoring arrangements.

The Community and Voluntary Pillar propose a range of specific targets for life expectancy, reduction of infant mortality and the establishment of mechanisms for health impact assessments. The Pillar also proposes the immediate implementation of a number of key policy commitments including the National Traveller Health Strategy and the Report of the Task Force on Suicide.

Chapter 10

People's experiences of the health services

Introduction

About one fifth (21 per cent) of submissions from organisations report on people's experiences of the health services and make recommendations as to what would need to be done in order to create a more people-centred health service.

The need for responsive, flexible, needs-led services, delivered in a manner which is respectful of people's needs and particular circumstances, is the core theme running through this material. The theme of access to services comes through in this material also. Much of the material deals with concerns about the experience of people from marginalised groups or communities.

Virtually all of the submissions dealing with this issue propose training for staff to equip them to work with service users in new kinds of ways that reflect the principles of a people-centred health service.

The main concerns and priorities in the submissions were the following:

• Access to information about services and entitlements

• Attitudes to services users

• The need for culturally appropriate services.

Access to information about services and entitlements

There was a general call for more information for the public on both services and entitlements. Information should be provided in ways that are sensitive to the needs and circumstances of those seeking the information. Information should be provided in accessible formats. It should be simple, free of jargon and culturally relevant. Multiple formats should be used, which take account of the range of ways in which communication happens in an increasingly diverse society.

The groups for whom information must be especially geared to their circumstances are people with sensory impairment, refugees and asylum seekers, women, women refugees, women living in violent situations, carers and older people. The Refugee Reception Agency provides a detailed analysis of the information needs of refugees and asylum seekers.

Reporting on its consultation process with parents in preparing its submission to the Health Strategy, Barnardos captures the essence of the submissions on the topic of information:

> *Many parents experienced difficulty in accessing information about entitlements, family planning, general health and nutrition. They cited an over-dependence on the written word, which did not take account of literacy difficulties as a common problem. The now familiar concept of the 'one-stop-shop' is commonly proposed as a solution to all information needs, but increasingly it is clear*

that many methods and media are needed and many channels are available, which could be used to greater effect...What is often lacking is not information per se but skilled and informed contact people to make the necessary links between the need and the appropriate response.

Among the proposals for information delivery systems are suggestions for delivery through voluntary organisations, greater use of pharmacies and post offices as information sources.

Culturally appropriate services

Several submissions outline the need for culturally appropriate services that take account of the needs of particular groups, including new groups in a society that is becoming increasingly diverse and multi-cultural. The focus is on responsiveness to gender, age, customs and beliefs and literacy levels.

For refugees and asylum seekers, practical responses would include access to interpreters, access to culturally sensitive personnel, orientation to Ireland and Irish services.

The Irish AIDS and Mobility Network believes that the sexual health problems faced by mobile population groups in the EU must be addressed with culturally appropriate services.

The Traveller Health Unit in the Western Health Board wishes to see the provision of an on-site advocate for Travellers and administrative procedures that take account of the fact of poor literacy skills.

Attitudes to service users

The topic of attitudes towards service users elicits some quite strong views and a sense of anger. Although many positive proposals are made, there is also a thread of analysis highlighting what people see as significant difficulties in attitudes to service users. There is reference in submissions to arrogance, insensitivity, inflexibility, judgmental and disrespectful attitudes to people.

Some of the aspects of the interaction between service user and provider where change is needed include:

- The need for people to have a say in matters to do with their treatment

- The need to know what is happening

- User-friendly systems and procedures in hospitals

- Procedures that take account of the needs of deaf people and people who are visually impaired

- Ways of avoiding having to give the same information 'over and over again'

- Responses to complaints or dissatisfaction.

Several groups discuss attitudes to their particular group. These include young people, men who have experienced violence, older people and women.

The Canteen organisation, a support group for young people with cancer, speaks about the need for doctors to 'talk to people, not at them'.

The submission from AMEN, the support organisation for male victims of domestic abuse, also expresses a good deal of concern about attitudes to its members in contacts with health services:

The experience of abused men with the health services are similar to those with the legal and justice system. Essentially they are met with disbelief, a reluctance to take them seriously and in some cases ridicule.

The organisation Age and Opportunity is concerned about reports that older people are often treated with condescension. It sees a need for for anti-ageism training and anti-discrimination training within the health services.

The vulnerability of people who are ill comes though in some submissions. A community group comments that "it is terrible to hear a person say that he/she is afraid to ask for something for fear of being 'given out to".

The need for user-friendly and accessible complaints procedures is raised in many submissions. This matter is treated very comprehensively by Patient Focus, the national voluntary patient advocacy organisation. Patient Focus offers a detailed analysis of people's experiences with health services and makes recommendations for advocacy and regulation of practice. These include proposals for:

- An independent, fully funded national agency to provide advocacy, mediation and liaison services at individual and strategic levels

- A charter of rights and actions to support the implementation of those rights

- New regulatory provisions including new Medical Council structures with at least 50 per cent lay membership and one fifth of that number drawn from patient advocacy organisations.

Comhairle is concerned about the absence of formal means of complaint about health services. In particular, it mentions the need for an appeals system relating to decisions about medical cards, evaluations of patient satisfaction and the publication of promised charters.

A number of organisations raise the question of the appointment of an Ombudsman for the Health and Social Services and would see this as a positive development.

PART 3

Views and proposals from health boards

Introduction 115

**Chapter 1: Executive summary of the views and proposals
from health board members** 116

**Chapter 2: Executive summary of the views and proposals
from health board management and staff** 121

Introduction

Extensive consultation was undertaken in each of the ten health boards and the Eastern Regional Health Authority (ERHA). The consultation process was led in each board by a senior officer nominated by the Chief Executive Officer to plan and manage the consultation process in that board (see Appendix 1) and to ensure it accurately reflected the views of the stakeholders. This group of co-ordinators, together with representatives of the facilitators employed by the Health Services National Partnership Forum[1] worked with Project Team members and with the consultant responsible for the overall consultation process. The aim of this joint work was to develop a national framework for the consultation plan for health service personnel.

The consultation process was hampered by the restrictions on meetings and travel relating to foot-and-mouth disease prevention arrangements and the relatively short time scale available for the work. Nonetheless, a very wide-ranging and intensive consultation took place.

Generally, the consultation took place at several levels including staff, management and governance (health board or authority members), but excluding the Chief Executive Officers who made their submissions through the Steering Group process.

The boards used a range of consultation methods. These included the following:

- Personal letters to all staff bringing the consultation process to their attention and asking for their views

- Facilitated workshops for staff dealing with particular care groups

- Facilitated workshops or meetings for members of the boards

- Questionnaires and opportunities for written inputs.

The outcome was a series of detailed reports from each of the ten health boards and the Eastern Regional Health Authority (ERHA). This report contains a summary of the views from health board members, management and staff expressed in these reports.

Chapter 1 contains an executive summary of the views and proposals from health board members; chapter 2 provides an executive summary of the views and proposals from health board management and staff. While it is not possible to reflect all the views and proposals expressed during the consultation, the main points raised are summarised under a number of headings which it is hoped will make the information easily accessible.

1 The **Health Services National Partnership Forum** is a body set up under the terms of Partnership 2000 to enhance the partnership between trade unions and management in the health sector.

Chapter 1

Executive summary of the views and proposals from health board members

Health promotion/population health

There is strong support among board members for a strengthened emphasis on population health with a major shift towards early intervention and prevention measures. Proposals include:

- Develop new focus on personal and community responsibilities in respect of population health and health status

- Introduce new measures to deal with social deprivation and exclusion

- Achieve closer inter-sectoral working between government departments and local authority sectors

- Develop programmes to promote physical exercise

- Facilitate regular health checks and screening

- Shift the emphasis of health promotion services to reflect a 'broader view,' focusing on lifestyle, alcohol, smoking, drugs, road traffic accidents and obesity

- Develop health promotion in school settings including the provision of school meals and breakfast clubs.

Care in the community

Health board members wish to see a strengthened role for primary care, as well as more flexible, user-friendly and efficient services. They propose:

- Expansion of eligibility for primary care as a priority

- Expansion of GP services within the framework of primary care

- Primary care practitioners including GPs, nurses, pharmacists operating as part of a team

- Improved integration of primary care services with the acute sector

- Development of a 24-hour all day, every day primary care service to meet the needs of the population

- Focused investment programme to provide facilities such as community nursing units, step down/rehabilitation beds, respite services, home supports

- Introduction of universal patient registration to improve information flow and enhance patient care

- Location of the full range of community services under one roof

- New systems and work practices that support good information sharing.

Acute hospitals and emergency services

Health board members expressed concerns about the acute hospital system as a whole, as well as specific concerns about A&E services. They also had particular concerns about its interface with the primary care system. The main proposals were as follows:

- Invest more resources to increase capacity (with particular regard to specialist services in the ERHA hospitals and the larger centres across the country)

- Develop hospital networks with well-defined service responsibilities

- Develop network of sub-acute services to complement services provided in an acute setting

- Improve local access to out-patient and day services

- Review admissions policies so as to improve access for acutely ill patients to hospital beds

- Develop separate medical admission units to reduce hospital admissions through A&E units

- Increase investment in service development in rehabilitation, convalescent care and respite care to meet needs of patients on discharge

- Increase existing A&E services to meet needs and demands

- Address inappropriate use of A&E services

- Tackle abuse of alcohol and its impact on vital A&E and emergency services

- Exploit new technologies to support more equitable distribution of and easier access to diagnostic services through the use of telemedicine etc

- Achieve optimum use of physical capacity through 24-hour, 7 day theatre work, consultant provided rather than consultant led service provision and improved discharge planning

- Introduce a strategy to address equity of access issues. Existing 'two-tier' system seen as inequitable. The existing incentive systems need to be assessed in terms of how they impact on equity of access within the existing system. Any barriers to access identified in contractual arrangements with providers need to be addressed as part of this.

Continuing care (all the key care groups)

Board members expressed support for targeting health services at vulnerable groups including people living in poverty, older people, people with mental health problems, and people with disabilities. A lack of integration is also identified as a problem particularly in meeting the needs of certain patient groups in appropriate settings, e.g. rehabilitation services for older persons and young chronic sick services.

The following is a summary of the main proposals:

People living in Poverty

- New focus on housing

- Policies to tackle poor nutrition and smoking.

Services for older people

- Development of home support services, day and respite services and community nursing units

- Increased investment in housing policy in the form of home improvement schemes and the provision of sheltered accommodation

- Review of the financial and social needs of carers including an urgent review of the means test for the Carer's Allowance

- Greater equity in subventing persons availing of nursing home accommodation.

Mental health services

- Major development of infrastructure and services to address historic under-investment

- Completion of relocation of acute units to general hospital sites

- Improved community infrastructure to provide care in the community, e.g. respite care, drop-in-centres, user support networks, greater home supports

- Increased emphasis on employment training and job placement

- Development of a greater emphasis on promoting positive mental health

- Development of strategies on suicide prevention.

Services for people with disabilities

- Further development of community and residential facilities to meet the needs of each client and their family, including day care, respite and other support services

- Development of partnership principles to strengthen the voice of parents and clients in developing and planning services on an objective basis

- Improved transport systems, especially in rural areas.

Children and families

- Develop further services for children particularly in the area of primary care and early year services

- Address deficits in dental and orthodontic services for children and adolescents

- Ringfence resources for early intervention/prevention services.

Island populations and rural communities

- Develop services for the population living on the islands around our coasts and those living in remote rural areas, in particular address the need for improved primary care services and improved transportation

- Respond to the needs of those who speak Irish by ensuring that a certain proportion of staff can communicate in Irish.

Funding of/eligibility for health services

Board members held strong opinions on funding and eligibility. The following is a summary of the main points raised.

Funding

- Major investment in the infrastructure of health and social services to increase capacity

- Emphasis on the special needs of the Border/Midlands/Western (BMW) region and the large centres of population growth including the greater Dublin area, Cork City, Limerick and Galway

- Removal of bureaucratic barriers to urgent capital development programmes

- Increased revenue expenditure on health and social services to bring expenditure in line with OECD and EU levels

- Introduction of multi-annual budgeting to facilitate longer-term planning.

Eligibility

- Full eligibility for priority groups such as children, older people, and people with disabilities including mental health problems.

Human resources

Board members recommend a strong pro-active collective approach to supporting staff and improving their working environments. A new national human resource strategy should address the following:

- Workforce planning

- Personal training and development needs of staff

- Recruitment, induction and staff retention

- Organisational development and change management, including the development of a learning culture within the health services

- Health and welfare issues

- Equality and diversity policies

- Improved communications structures, development of teamwork and a multidisciplinary approach to healthcare delivery.

- A move to make permanent most temporary posts currently in the system.

Quality (including models for participation)

Underpinning all the proposals of board members is the need for a quality approach to healthcare. Essential ingredients are evidence-based guidelines, information support systems, empowered consumers, legislation, participation by staff and agreed performance indicators.

- Link quality to accreditation and standards through a formal programme

- Establish a national standards/accreditation body which would take the lead in driving the change involved in creating a quality culture

- Appoint a Health Ombudsman

- Improve the level of user involvement and participation in planning new services and in quality proofing the existing ones

- Establish consumer panels or stakeholder forums at a local service delivery level and at national policy making level to provide a real voice in the decision-making process for individuals

- Introduce feedback mechanisms such as satisfaction surveys

- Support staff to develop their skills to provide a better customer focus

- Focus on user need, including greater flexibility around opening hours and greater use of internet technologies, etc

- Audit current service provision to demonstrate value for money.

Organisation/infrastructure

Health board members propose a number of changes to improve existing organisation/infrastructure.

- Strengthened accountability of the management system through regular audit of management at all levels

- Wider representation on health boards to favour consumers

- Support for giving the health boards outside Dublin a seat on the Eastern Regional Health Authority (ERHA) to provide for a voice in relation to national and supra-regional services that are located in the ERHA region

- Ongoing consultations as part of the implementation framework for the Strategy

- Greater responsibility for organisations involved in healthcare delivery to take account of the inter-sectoral dimensions of health determinants and provide for meaningful inter-sectoral activity at national and local levels

- Clearer definition of roles and responsibilities of the various players within the health services – Department of Health and Children, Health Boards, ERHA, regulatory bodies, professional and training bodies, etc. At present there is a level of ambiguity and blurred accountability that impedes the freedom of managers to control their environment, to quickly free up resources and to action priorities

- Increased involvement of voluntary agencies and bodies in health and social service delivery by improving their formal links with, and possible representation on, health boards.

Chapter 2

Executive summary of views and proposals from health board management and staff

Health promotion/population health

There is strong support among health board staff for the development of a population health approach at all levels with a greater emphasis on prevention. Proposals include the following:

*   The introduction of an 'environmental impact statement' and a 'health impact statement' for all major developments, where appropriate

*   Health proofing of all major policies/plans of government departments/local authorities/public bodies

*   Provision of appropriate screening and preventive services free of charge

*   Introduction of specific anti-poverty measures to target vulnerable groups

*   More intensive initiatives in areas such as prevention of road traffic accidents and substance abuse

*   Promotion of physical exercise including pilot initiatives involving GPs and leisure centres

*   Focus on diet/nutrition

*   Tighter legislative constraints and improved inter-sectoral cooperation, including enforced age identification to control the sale of cigarettes and also to eliminate sponsorship by tobacco companies of sporting or lifestyle events

*   Greater use of school curriculum to promote improved health

*   Investment in up-to-date print and media material to increase awareness and promote healthy lifestyles

*   More resources for mental health promotion

*   Priority for vaccination programmes.

Care in the community

The development of primary care as a major element of the healthcare system is a priority. Many specific service developments are recommended throughout all of the care groups with the overall emphasis clearly on development supported by a population health approach that is monitored and evaluated. Proposals deal with access, special needs, linkages with other facets of the health system, improved flexibility and efficiency. Proposals include the following:

*   Restructuring of GP practices to incorporate a team of health professionals as well as on-site diagnostic facilities

- Provision of out-reach clinics by consultants in GP practices, thus bringing the delivery of the service closer to the patient

- Development of community nursing services with links to local GP and acute hospital services

- Extension of eligibility for primary care services

- Specialist support services for those with special needs e.g. older people

- More day services, home-based services, respite care, rehabilitation and step-down services

- Prioritisation of the development of primary care in line with the NAPS Strategy

- Improved co-ordination and integration between primary and acute care for special categories of patients e.g. patients with chronic medical conditions. Chronic illness protocols for asthma and diabetes should be developed

- The introduction of a 24-hour all day every day primary care service

- Better integration of out-of-hours GP services with the emergency pre-hospital services and the hospital services

- Recognition of specific challenges of primary care provision in a metropolitan setting, for example access to GP services in deprived area

- More focus on mental health issues within the primary care setting

- Development of protocols for investigation and referral to hospital out-patient departments between hospital consultants and GPs to promote an integrated service in an appropriate setting

- Introduction of an effective transport infrastructure

- Development of counselling/psychotherapy services

- More resources for community hospitals

- Appointment of liaison nursing staff in all hospitals to link with community services to plan discharge of patients back into the community

- One-stop shop for teenage health – incorporating sexual health, counselling, suicide prevention, career guidance information, etc

- Deregulation of pharmacies so as to improve access for the public.

Acute hospitals and emergency services

Serious concern was expressed about the absence of an overall strategic plan for acute care. Concerns and proposals addressed overall planning, admissions policies, consultant inputs, staffing and resources, physical facilities, quality management and linkages with other sectors of the healthcare system.

Proposals include the following:

- Introduce a major plan for acute hospital services with a strategy for national, supra-regional and regional services

- Increase the capacity of the existing acute hospital service system with particular reference to orthopaedics, ear, nose and throat (ENT) and ophthalmology

- Reduce waiting times for elective procedures

- Benchmark standards for admissions to waiting lists for key services. This could be done by a task force set up to deliver on standards, protocols and guidelines to deal with key services

- Improve standards of physical accommodation

- Allocate appointment times in hospital out-patient departments and extend opening hours

- Introduce policy of giving priority for hospital admission for non-national and non-regional specialties to persons in the hospital catchment area

- Attach observation wards to all A&E departments

- Develop a clear policy statement on the appropriate balance between public/private patient workloads within the publicly funded system

- Examine contractual arrangements with consultants to ensure a more equitable approach to the delivery of services. Eliminate cross-subsidisation in the acute sector

- Work towards a situation where all private and semi-private beds would be in a separate building, ideally on an acute hospital site

- Purchase appropriate services for public patients from the private sector

- Manage consultant manpower more effectively, with reviews of units and practices of consultants and key professionals in crucial service areas

- Reduce waiting times for those needing A&E services

- Increase emphasis on consultant-provided care in A&E departments and the implementation of triage systems throughout all aspects of the emergency services

- Create specialist nursing posts such as advanced nurse practitioners to improve services in A&E

- Develop an equipment replacement policy and infrastructure development plan

- Use information technology to expand and develop telematic services as well as out-reach and out-patient services

- Extend opening hours of departments such as radiology and laboratory to 16 hours a day 6 days a week

- Examine possibility of using old or retired facilities or introducing mobile or temporary facilities to deal with the backlogs

- Increase use of cross border services

- Consider contracts within the EU for identified services

- Develop a convalescence care programme to facilitate early discharge

- Increase the number of neurologists to provide an adequate service.

Continuing care services (all the key care groups)

Health board management and staff are strongly in support of addressing health needs of people who are disadvantaged due to their geographic location and level of income. A number of proposals were made in connection with specific groups including people living in poverty, older people, people with mental health problems, people with disabilities and children.

People living in poverty

- Address poor nutrition

- Target resources at housing and accommodation needs.

Services for older people

- Develop new models of care in the home setting

- Provide more home care and community-based supports

- Increase the Carer's Allowance and other financial support

- Increase day respite, home support services and residential facilities

- Develop two levels of rehabilitation for older people – acute rehabilitation beds on the acute hospital site and adequate step-down facilities where longer-term rehabilitation can be provided

- Increase nursing home subvention and simplify means test process

- Increase accountability and standardise costs in nursing homes

- Acknowledge social needs of carers by providing twilight, weekend cover and sitting services

- Develop mental health services for older people

- Provide art and music therapy for people with dementia

- Incorporate alternative medicine into the care of older people

- Provide a geriatric unit attached to all general hospitals.

Mental health services

- Develop strategies to prevent suicide and associated problems

- Develop mental health services in the community including home care and outreach services

- Acute psychiatric services should be increasingly integrated on the acute hospital site to encourage the 'de-institutionalisation' of patients

- Develop 24-hour crisis intervention services

- Increase emphasis on employment, training and job placement.

Services for people with disabilities

- Improve home support services including respite care

- Improve transport systems and access to buildings

- Develop partnership principles in this service area

- Provide additional funding for autism services

- Provide appropriate rehabilitation facilities for young chronically disabled including people with head injuries, multiple sclerosis and Parkinson's disease

- Provide special sheltered accommodation for young chronically disabled. Long-term care facilities are not suitable for this group.

Child and family services

- Develop early years services for children

- Establish formal inter-departmental/inter-agency co-operation particularly where services overlap with housing, recreation/diversion activities, education etc

- Provide additional resources for speech and language therapy and dental services (including orthodontics).

Other groups

Homeless people

- Establish additional drop-in centres in Dublin in association with Dublin Corporation and County Councils.

Asylum seekers

- Greater flexibility including cross-cultural training for healthcare workers to foster understanding of the different needs of patients from divergent cultures

- Increased weekly welfare allowance and removal of restrictions in relation to employment.

Substance abuse

- More support for families of alcohol/drug abuse clients

- More accessible treatment units across the country.

Travellers' health

- Publish Travellers' Health Strategy as a matter of priority

- Establish a specific community nursing service for Travellers.

Women's health

- Extend breast screening to the 40+ age group

- Provide range of complementary health services.

Men's health

- Provide local health screening for men

- Provide health promotion in schools which includes a gender focus for boys.

Adolescent health

- Health lifestyle education at school, especially drugs, alcohol, dental, sex education

- Free medical care.

Funding of health services

There is strong support for increased levels of funding, both capital and revenue. Management and staff hold the view that significant investment is required on the revenue side to bring the level of investment in health in Ireland to the level that obtains within the EU and OECD. Specific proposals include the following:

- A greater percentage of GNP needs to be allocated to bring level of funding up to European average

- Greater investment in the rural areas and the Border/Midlands/Western region

- Greater investment in the Eastern Region to address significant challenges arising from the continued growth of the population

- A review of basic core services to assess needs for additional funding

- Review of the funding arrangements and the planning arrangements for major and minor capital infrastructure development. Health board managers and staff are seeking more flexibility in respect of smaller projects and a more aggressive approach to the delivery of major projects

- Abolition of Department of Health and Children guidelines for minor projects and increased EU limits on expenditure

- Development of funding model to relate more closely to service planning requirements

- Move to multi-annual budgeting cycle that incorporates capital investment

- Introduction of funding for depreciation costs as part of overall resourcing and a scheduled programme for equipment replacement.

Eligibility for health services

- Provide clarity on entitlement versus eligibility within the fixed budget environment

- Introduce a simplified and standardised system for determining eligibility for all health and personal social services

- Increase income thresholds for medical card eligibility

- Introduce free medical care for particular groups, irrespective of income, e.g. cancer patients, children, adolescents, older people

- Introduce system of graded entitlements.

Human resources

A clear need for a human resource strategy for the health services was identified. Important elements of such a strategy should include:

- Establishment of a task force to support the recruitment and retention of staff at all levels and to ensure a more responsive approach from statutory and regulating bodies on issues such as accreditation, approvals, etc

- Allow more flexibility at board level to decide on numbers/grades of staff within overall budget of health agency

- Link regulatory/training bodies within formal national manpower planning structure

- Reduce elements of clinical training which lead to segregation of disciplines. Consider a common 'core year' for health workers

- Ringfence funding for training and development of staff

- Review the common recruitment pool, as it is perceived to be discriminatory by staff and an obstacle to career development and change in the health services

- Examine proposals to make, on a once off basis, existing temporary employees permanent so as to aid in the retention of staff at all levels

- Provide training in customer services for all staff

- Give a role to the educational institutes in ensuring sufficient training places are available to meet service needs

- Create additional career opportunities between the levels of non consultant hospital doctor and consultant

- Address health and welfare issues, including provision of a safe work environment

- Provide child care and leisure facilities

- Review recruitment policies within general practice. There is a need to introduce job sharing, sessional work and career breaks

- Introduce reward system linked to performance

- Introduce more flexitime/term time working.

Quality (including models for participation)

There is agreement that quality should be seen as an ongoing and continuous process supported by the development of quality guidelines and protocols. Proposals for enhancing the quality of service include the following:

- Improved quality systems, including systems for monitoring and evaluation

- Accreditation, benchmarking and continuous quality assurance

- Greater transparency of decision making

- Improved clinical governance and audit

- Comparative analysis and benchmarking with health services internationally

- Development of implementation strategies

- Establishment of mechanisms for community inputs into the planning and delivery of services

- Improved customer and complaint management procedures

- Establishment of a Health Ombudsman's Office

- Identification of mechanisms for linking funding to performance measures of quality and impact

- Partnership structures to incorporate views of users of the services

- Establishment of mechanisms such as hospital accreditation, patient satisfaction surveys and patient advocacy programmes to promote information use, quality care and patient empowerment

- Lead role for the Department of Health and Children in commissioning quality surveys and guarantee follow-through on the findings of such surveys

- A new post of 'Patient Liaison Officer' in agencies whose remit would be the introduction of standardised protocols and procedures to deal with the queries and complaints of patients and their families

- An independent inspectorate with powers to report on each service area.

Health information systems

Proposals deal with improved information systems for strategic planning as well as with better information for service users. They are as follows:

- Resource and implement the proposed Health Information Strategy without delay

- Provide funding for high quality, accurate, relevant and meaningful information at all points of the decision making process in the health system

- Develop a patient identification number system

- Improve access to information available to patients and clients on services and entitlements

- Harness internet technologies for the effective delivery of information within the health service to all clients.

Organisation/infrastructure

There is a need to review and clarify the roles of existing statutory and regulatory organisations and to improve integration and responsiveness of the whole system. Proposals include the following:

*   Put in place a clear policy framework, defining the role of key services, and an implementation plan, with resources to address strategic objectives set out in the Strategy

*   Modernise health services management and improve its effectiveness

*   Introduce an independent overview of organisational and management structures

*   Introduce strategic planning and evidence-based decision-making throughout the whole system

*   Develop greater transparency of decision-making and a high-level commitment to performance management, standards and the quality of patient care at all levels

*   Develop mechanism for building in consumer involvement in decision-making

*   Look at the total service and the response of the whole system of healthcare

*   Improve coordination between government departments, Department of Health and Children and health boards

*   Improve coordination between county development boards and health boards

*   Reduce bureaucracy and red tape.

Conclusion

This Report is a summary of the views and proposals expressed by board members, management and staff of the health boards during the consultation process which was undertaken as part of the development of the Health Strategy.

The material in the reports proved to be extremely wide-ranging and contributed in a number of ways to the development of the Strategy. While some of the issues raised are reflected in the views of the public and organisations, the material summarised in this section provides a perspective from people working in the system which is extremely valuable. The full reports of the various boards can be obtained directly from the headquarters of each health board or via the relevant website.

PART 4

Views and proposals from staff of the Department of Health and Children

Introduction

The consultation process carried out with the staff of the Department of Health and Children (DoHC) was facilitated by the Institute of Public Administration (IPA). It consisted of 14 day-long sessions in which staff were asked their views and proposals both as consumers of the health services and as members of staff. A total of 409 out of 520 staff participated.

6 questions were put to staff members during the consultation sessions:

1. *What strategic changes would have the greatest benefit for people's health and well-being, in your opinion?*

2. *If extra money was to be invested in health and well-being, what should the priorities be for spending that money?*

3. *Have you any other views or proposals for the new Health Strategy?*

4. *What are your views on the role of the Department of Health and Children and what changes would you suggest to improve the effectiveness of the Department?*

5. *What changes would you suggest to improve the effectiveness of existing structures?*

6. *What changes or developments would you recommend in your service area to provide a better service for the public or your customers?*

This report is based on the analysis of the responses received to questions 1, 2 and 3. The views and proposals expressed by staff in response to these 3 questions have been merged under a number of key themes. While it has not been possible to include all the individual concerns raised during the consultation process this summary encompasses the major issues of concern to staff.

Responses to questions 4, 5 and 6 have also been analysed and the key themes identified from that process will feed into the independent review and subsequent restructuring of the Department which will follow the publication of the Health Strategy.

In order of priority, the areas identified by staff as requiring strategic change were:

1. **Improved access to health services**

2. **Reform of accident and emergency services and out-patient services**

3. **Further development of health promotion**

4. **Primary care reform**

5. **Improved quality/accountability at all levels**

A small number of views which does not fit under any of the above is listed under the **"other proposals"** category on page 135.

The proposals put forward by staff are presented in the form of bullet points.

Improved access to health services

Staff in the Department of Health and Children wish to see access to health services improved for all and a fair and equitable health system provided. They identify groups whose needs should be met as a matter of priority. They wish to see short-term measures adopted to address urgent shortfalls. They also see a need for long-term structural change through changes in entitlements and higher investment in staffing:

- Reduce waiting lists for all services

- Eliminate the 'two-tier' system

- In the short term use private beds for public patients

- Re-examine the common contract with all medical consultants

- Extend medical card eligibility to all children and adolescents under 18 years of age

- Extend medical card eligibility to all persons aged over 65

- Target new resources to areas of economic or geographic inequalities in health services or health status

- Improve access to services for older people, people with disabilities, people who are homeless or disadvantaged, children at risk, immigrants and asylum seekers

- Improve access to palliative care services

- Increase capacity by appointing more healthcare professionals and administrative staff at all levels

- Provide clear information on entitlements and availability of services

- Clarify entitlements under private health insurance schemes offered by different providers

- Provide longer and more flexible opening hours for all services

- Examine entry requirements for health professions to reduce barriers to entry.

Accident and emergency and out-patient services

Proposals included improvements in A&E services cover, long-term investment in facilities, restructured management of the care processes and more user-friendly and accessible systems:

- Provide additional capital investment to build new facilities, upgrade existing facilities, including A&E departments and replace medical equipment. Capital budgets should be linked to inflation

- Appoint consultant directors who would have full responsibility for clinical/general management of all A&E units

- Create highly visible consultant-led teams

- Provide for GPs and other appropriate health professionals to work in A&E units in certain circumstances

- Initiate a radical redesign of waiting areas to include safe and supervised environments including the provision of separate areas for 'drinking and drug-related illnesses'

- Introduce longer and more flexible working/opening hours

- Encourage a policy of assisting patients to keep appointments e.g. schedule appointment to suit the patient.

Health promotion

There is a need for a plan with a broad, cross-sectoral approach to health and increased investment in health promotion and illness prevention strategies:

- Development and implementation of a health promotion plan aimed at lowering the incidence of lifestyle-related illnesses

- Health gain impact of all health policies should be assessed

- Substantial increase in funding, including transfer of taxes collected from tobacco sales into the health promotion budget

- Greater emphasis on education and information on healthy lifestyle choices at primary school level and for other target groups

- Additional funding for research into lifestyle-related illnesses

- More health screening

- Improved implementation of strategies such as the Cancer Strategy and the Cardiovascular Strategy.

Primary care

A strategy for improved primary care should be developed and include improved access to GP services, a team-based approach to provision, priority for groups with special needs and improved linkages within and between services:

- Reduce the waiting lists in all areas of primary care

- Increase availability of GP services

- Create the environment to attract and retain more GPs in rural areas

- Create a climate to encourage GPs and dental services to team up with other healthcare professionals and provide 24-hour/weekend openings in appropriate client driven areas (one-stop shop approach)

- Support GPs to carry out appropriate procedures at surgery level

- Appoint more community-based nurses and provide a career structure to retain them

- Improve and increase availability of local community hospitals and outreach clinics and provide more specialist services at a regional level

- Provide more support services, including home-based support and sheltered housing for the elderly so that they can be cared for in the community

- Provide greater financial and other support for carers

- Improve community-based family support interventions

- Improve availability of rehabilitation, respite, 'step-down' facilities

- Provide full access for marginal groups including Travellers, homeless people, the disadvantaged and ethnic minorities

- Promote an inter-sectoral approach to primary care with better linkages to local hospital services

- Improve co-operation between different disciplines, e.g. GPs, public health nurses

- Improve linkages and communication systems within and between services so as to provide a 'seamless' service

- Provide better transport systems to and from primary care services

- Provide greater use of complementary medicine.

Quality/accountability

New systems are needed to enhance quality and to improve accountability. The Department of Health and Children should be equipped to take a lead role in developing quality systems and in strengthening accountability at all levels. The development of integrated, seamless services is an essential feature of quality:

- Ensure that responsibility for the full implementation of the Health Strategy rests with DoHC

- Set realistic targets in consultation with health boards and other agencies, provide for a professional review process and establish evaluation tools and systems

- Examine existing structures of DoHC and health boards to determine their capacity to deliver on or implement the Health Strategy

- Examine structures to ensure that regional and local health needs are not discriminated against

- Establish a lead role for DoHC in requiring accountability for funding provided to health boards and other agencies and design systems of ensuring 'value for money'

- Establish a 'value for money' unit within DoHC

- Establish accountability for personal performance, in the context of all aspects of service delivery, as a primary goal

- Provide international standards, comparisons and evaluation tools and methods

- Encourage and reward the provision of quality customer/client care

- Appoint a Health Ombudsman

- Develop information services, which will also source the services appropriate for individual needs in a 'one-stop shop' approach

- Develop a 'seamless approach' to the provision of all health services on a national and local level

- Develop a health service-wide IT strategy

- Improve communication between DoHC, other government departments and health boards/agencies.

Other proposals

- Provide capital grants for additional nursing home places

- Initiate a national development plan in palliative care and a hospice programme

- Expand early intervention measures for children

- Set up a national programme for voluntarism

- Develop a human resources strategy, to include training, development and performance management retention strategies

- Provide for and build on relationships between North/South bodies.

Conclusion

This report is the result of a synthesis of the information collected over the fourteen staff consultations. It reflects the wide range of views put forward by staff in the Department of Health and Children.

It is not intended to summarise here all the issues raised but it is significant to note that they include, for example, a refocusing of health services on primary care and health promotion, a need to re-examine the 'two-tier' system, more resources for existing services, in particular A&E services and longer opening hours. They include a clear message about implementation and evaluation and the need for a 'value for money' approach. Meeting the needs of groups such as older people and children also receives high priority.

PART 5

Report of the consultation process undertaken by the Working Group on the National Anti-Poverty Strategy (NAPS) and Health

The context of NAPS and Health

The National Anti-Poverty Strategy (NAPS) was published in 1997. It originated from a Government commitment to the development of an anti-poverty strategy at the UN World Social Summit in Copenhagen in 1995.

The NAPS set a 10-year programme for poverty reduction and outlined five areas of focus. These areas were income adequacy, unemployment, educational disadvantage, urban concentrations of poverty and rural poverty. The NAPS set an overall global poverty reduction target, alongside five other targets in the above areas. While health issues were outlined in the original NAPS, no specific health targets were set. However, the NAPS did oblige all government departments to take the reduction of poverty into account in their strategic planning process and poverty proofing was introduced across all government policies. Under the Programme for Prosperity and Fairness (PPF), the NAPS is being reviewed and new targets will be set in 'health' and 'accommodation/housing', while targets in the other areas are being revised. Poverty proofing is to be extended in a phased manner at local level through local authorities and health boards. The PPF also contains a commitment to develop an implementation and monitoring framework for the NAPS and health targets.

This NAPS review is also taking place in the context of the development of National Action Plans against Poverty and Social Exclusion (NAP incl) by each EU member state to achieve the objectives in the Fight against Poverty and Social Exclusion set in Nice in December, 2000. The NAPS review will feed into the NAP incl.

The commitment in the PPF to set NAPS targets for health was particularly timely in the context of the development of the new Health Strategy which has equity as one of its key principles. It was indicated at the outset that the NAPS health targets and associated monitoring and implementation framework would form an important strand in the new Strategy.

The aim of the NAPS health targets is to reduce health inequalities and associated poverty. The link between poverty and health is well established. Poorer people experience poorer health. Poverty is known to contribute to poor health directly, for example, through inadequate housing or poor environments and indirectly, for example, through poor diet or stress. Being poor also makes it more difficult to access or afford healthcare and reduces the opportunity for adopting a healthy lifestyle.

Some groups experience particularly poor health. For example, Travellers are known to have very high infant mortality rates and low life expectancy. There is also growing concern about the health of refugees and asylum seekers. As well as the wide gap in the health of rich and poor as demonstrated by many studies in Ireland and elsewhere, there is also strong consistent evidence of a gradient in health favouring those higher up the socio-economic scale.

Working Group on NAPS and Health

To progress the issue of setting NAPS targets for health, the Department of Health and Children established a Working Group on NAPS and Health in Autumn 2000. Membership included the representatives from the Social Partners: Farmers, Unions, Community and Voluntary Sector, Industry/Business/relevant government departments; the health boards and health service providers; the Combat Poverty Agency (CPA) and the Institute of Public Health in Ireland (IPH). The Working Group was chaired by the Chief Medical Officer of the Department of Health and Children, Dr Jim Kiely.

Consultation process for NAPS and Health

The Government had indicated its wish to make the NAPS review process as inclusive as possible. The Department engaged the assistance of the Institute of Public Health (IPH) for the research and consultative aspects of the process. (The Institute's brief includes the issues of health inequalities and strengthening partnerships for health). The Working Group embarked on a wide ranging consultation which included the following elements:

- A public call for submissions in national newspapers on 20th February, 2001

- A targeted call for submissions to over 200 organisations and networks with a brief relevant to NAPS and Health

- Consultation process by regional health boards, in conjunction with their consultations for the Health Strategy

- Gathering information through the networks and constituent organisations of the Community and Voluntary Pillar and the development by the Pillar of a composite report

- Gathering information through city and county development boards

- Providing resources for advocacy groups and organisations to encourage direct consultation with excluded people

- Hosting a national 'checkback' seminar in June, 2001.

The consultation process was facilitated by the Institute of Public Health, which set up a support team made up of members of the Working Group. A NAPS/Health webpage (www.doh.ie/naps) was established on the Department's website at the outset of the consultation and a Lo-call answering facility was provided. To avoid duplication the NAPS/Health consultation was coordinated with that for the Health Strategy.

Breakdown of submissions by type (organisations and individual):

151 submissions were received from the different strands of the consultation process. There were 131 written submissions, 10 oral (received through the Lo-Call comment line), 9 submissions from organisations who attended a consultative seminar hosted by the Community and Voluntary Pillar, and 1 video. 27 came from private individuals, 124 came from organisations. A majority of submissions came from voluntary and community organisations, networks and projects, with other submissions received from the health boards, statutory bodies, religious groups, trade unions, doctors, academics, city and county development boards, local area partnerships, a political party and a range of other organisations. A report (see last paragraph of this document for details) summarising the submissions has been prepared and includes a list of organisations which participated and feedback from the 'checkback' seminar.

Content of responses

The call for submissions was supported by a series of prompt questions. These asked what were the main things that affect the health of people living in poverty and/or social exclusion, negatively and positively and what improvements need to happen to help people most in need to be healthier. Questions were then asked specifically on the three areas upon which the Working Group had decided to focus its attention, i.e.

- The influence of public policies generally on people's health

- Equity of access to health and personal social services

- Information and research needed to support the development and monitoring of NAPS targets for the health sector.

A social model of health

A large number of the submissions emphasised the need for a more holistic, broader social model of health which encompasses the concept of social gain and is concerned with quality of life. The utilisation of such a model would recognise the critical role of the broad social determinants of health, place greater emphasis on health promotion and prevention and on supporting people in caring for their own health, recognise the value of existing family and social networks in doing this and recognise the potential contribution of complementary therapies alongside conventional medical approaches.

Factors identified as influencing health

The main factors identified in the submissions as influencing health are listed below – firstly the general social determinants and then the health service factors.

Social determinants of health – negative influences

- Poverty and social exclusion were identified as critical factors influencing physical and mental ill health. There was particular emphasis on psychological stress, distress, physical and social isolation caused by poverty and social exclusion

- Low income, unemployment and low social welfare rates

- Income inequality and social inequality caused by recent economic growth

- Lack of access to and poor quality of health and other public services (see section below for information on health services)

- Poor environmental conditions, including housing, roads and transport, lack of recreational and community facilities and amenities and depressing surroundings

- The lack and poor quality of accommodation provision, particularly for Travellers

- Poor quality and lack of public housing, affordable housing and supportive housing

- Racism and discrimination

- The lack of, and inadequacy of, mechanisms used to engage and involve citizens and communities, who are living in poverty or experiencing social exclusion, in decision-making on policy and programme development

- The policy development process

- The circumstances of women who live in poverty, who are considered at particular risk, as they often put the health and well-being of their children and families before their own

- Lack of, and inaccessibility of, information on rights and entitlements

- Inadequate public transport and, in particular, the lack of it in rural areas

- Lack of family and community supports (informal and formal)

- Educational disadvantage, low levels of literacy, poor school attendance, low expectations of achievement and early school leaving

- The absence of a rights-based approach to economic and social policy development

- Lack of coherence and collaboration between sectors on policies and programmes relevant to poverty and health

- Current funding procedures which can militate against multi-sectoral work and long-term planning.

Social determinants of health - positive influences

The positive influences outlined were generally the opposite to those mentioned above with a strong focus on the importance of:

- Family, community and social support networks

- Employment and adequate income levels

- More redistributive tax and welfare policies which support people living in poverty or experiencing social exclusion

- Good quality accessible health and other public services

- Healthy living environments including good quality public housing and accommodation

- Educational opportunities for all

- Equality and anti-discrimination policies and legislation

- Good, accessible public transport

- Information on rights, entitlements and services.

Health service factors identified as influencing health

While there was a broad interpretation in the submissions of what influences health, the role of health services in positively or negatively impacting on people's health was outlined in some detail, with particular emphasis on:

- the importance of primary healthcare

- eligibility issues, e.g. having a medical card

- the 'two-tier' health system benefiting those who need it least

- waiting lists and times, waiting for assessment for use of services and for aids and appliances

- the fact that the health system is overburdened

- the need for health service providers to consult with citizens and communities, particularly those who are most marginalised and/or most in need of health services

- information on services and entitlements (particularly for people with low literacy levels or low English language comprehension)

- information on living a healthy life and health promotion

- healthy living/community centres supporting people's health, community development approach to health

- the importance of social supports, particularly informal supports of family and friends

- distance from health services and/or inadequate transport

- fear of health professionals and their use of inaccessible language

- inflexible opening hours

- geographical inequality in service provision

- lack of integration between different parts of the health service

- overreliance on families and carers for caring.

Recommendations for improvements and change

Recommendations for improvements and change are summarised below under the topics:

- Public policies generally

- Equity of access to health and personal social services

- Information and research needed to support the development and monitoring of NAPS targets for the health sector.

A number of cross-cutting issues relevant across different areas of the health services and, in many cases, across the wider public service were also identified and are presented later in the document

Public policies generally

Impact of poverty and social exclusion on health

Very many submissions stressed the link between poverty, social exclusion and health and therefore efforts to tackle these are seen as key to improving the health of people who are living in situations of poverty or social exclusion. Increased social welfare rates and an increased minimum wage to ensure sufficient income for all, particularly the most vulnerable, were mentioned as the most fundamental ways of positively influencing people's health. There is also a focus in the submissions on the need to address income inequality and reduce the gap between the rich and poor, through more redistributive tax and welfare policies. There was a particular concern expressed for children in poverty with specific mention also of the needs of older people, women in poverty, people with disabilities and carers. Concern was also expressed for the situation of Travellers, refugees and asylum seekers and homeless people.

There was reference to the need to eliminate 'the poverty trap' by allowing people to maintain benefits and entitlements when making the transition from welfare to work.

Accommodation/housing and the environment

An increased provision and maintenance of good quality public housing, affordable housing and sheltered housing and accommodation emerged as an important factor which would improve the health of those living in poverty and experiencing social exclusion.

The need to dramatically improve the living conditions on Travellers' sites, their accommodation and support services was clearly outlined. So too were the developments necessary to adequately provide services for homeless people, in particular those with addictions. The need for extending provision of social, sheltered and supported housing is a consistent theme throughout the submissions particularly for the more vulnerable sections of the population in need of care and support, specifically on health matters. This applies in particular to older people, people with disabilities and people with mental health problems released from institutions.

Concern was expressed in relation to the dispersal policy for refugees and asylum seekers and how these further perpetuate poor health among this group. The ghettoisation of parts of cities and towns was raised and the importance of building housing estates where there is an infrastructure to support the people in that area - schools, shops, health services, transport, parks, sports and recreation facilities. Basic facilities such as footpaths and street lighting are outlined as small changes which could have a very positive impact on people's lives.

Health policies

Many of the submissions outlined the need for government policies in the area of health to focus on a broader concept of health and healthier public policy development as well as on health service provision. Specific health service and policy issues are dealt with in a later section.

Racism and discrimination

Action against racism and discrimination was deemed an essential component of developing a healthy society. There were recommendations that the provisions of the Equal Status Act be implemented in full with an accompanying education and awareness programme. The issue of discrimination was raised in a variety of submissions in relation to race, ethnicity, gender, disability, sexual orientation, where people live, age, etc.

Education and lifelong learning opportunities

The importance of education in enhancing people's health and well-being emerged as a common issue in many submissions, in particular how education can be a route out of poverty and therefore contribute to improving health. The range of issues covered includes the significant impact of pre-school; the importance of the primary and secondary school curriculum being relevant to students, in particular those who are most at risk; making third-level education more accessible; placing equal emphasis on vocational education; adult learning, literacy and numeracy courses available locally and the development of new community-based education models. A flexible, lifelong education system that is designed for, and accessible to, those most in need, particularly minorities, is distinctly emphasised. Many submissions recommend a holistic approach to education with equal emphasis being placed on the development of social and life skills as on academic achievement. Low literacy levels are mentioned as a significant barrier to access to information on both entitlements and health education as well as to the ability to communicate confidently with staff providing health or other services and to follow advice or read medicine labels. The provision of nutritious school meals, breakfast and after school clubs is recommended. Providing support for children and young people with special needs, particularly those with disabilities, and providing education and training for people with disabilities are highlighted in many of the submissions.

Transport

The need for improved provision of transport from marginalised rural and urban communities, with a particular focus on the inaccessibility of transport in rural areas, is a strong theme emerging from the submissions. There is considerable reference to the difficulty of accessing services either due to their distant location and/or the lack of transport. While this factor is mentioned most usually in relation to services in rural areas, it is also raised in relation to urban areas e.g. bus routes may not suit or elderly people may not be able to use public transport. A number of suggestions are made including: provision of services locally where possible; greater provision of outreach and mobile services; better co-ordination of service provision with local transport in rural areas; provision of vouchers for transport and, where necessary, for bed and breakfast and other meals; learning from community-based transport initiatives. The needs of people with disabilities and older people should be considered in all transport developments.

Equitable access to health and personal social services

A range of issues and recommendations emerged in relation to equitable access to health and personal social services as follows:

A move to a rights-based approach

Many submissions, particularly those coming from the Community and Voluntary Sector and state agencies with a remit around equality, emphasised the value of a move to a rights-based approach to health and healthcare and how framing the debate in a rights perspective could lead to the development of more responsive public policies. Support was expressed in a number of submissions for the insertion into the Constitution of the right to healthcare. Specific mention is made of children in the context of this right. There is also mention of how NAPS should be brought forward in the context of social and economic rights.

Eligibility/entitlements

There was frequent mention of an inequitable two-tier system and of the fact that access should be based on need and not on financial considerations. Positively, having a medical card was frequently mentioned as helping people to access services. Negatively, many referred to the deterrent effect of the costs involved on the use of services for those without a card, particularly for those just above the income guidelines. Paying the cost involved was cited as creating a poverty trap for those on low incomes and for people with disabilities. Submissions also indicated considerable concern with access to a medical card for children.

Many submissions recommended increasing the income threshold in the guidelines for the medical card. There was also a number of suggestions in relation to universal access, e.g. universal access to a comprehensive and adequately resourced primary healthcare service by 2007 with access to acute care, medical and paramedical treatments when required; a review of models from other countries which promote an equality-based approach; one suggestion for the introduction of a universal health insurance scheme whereby each individual would be insured on an equal footing for all necessary health services, including primary care as well as hospital and specialist services. There was a range of other suggestions in relation to the medical card including the following: automatic entitlement for certain groups – children were most frequently mentioned; having a tapered medical card; retention of the medical card on entering the labour market, e.g. for Travellers, people with disabilities; extending the range of services available on the medical card, e.g. cervical screening and counselling; simplified procedures for nomadic groups and asylum seekers.

Primary care

A comprehensive holistic, integrated and accessible primary care service is seen as fundamental to improving the health of people who are living in poverty or experiencing social exclusion. There is an emphasis on supporting people to take care of their own health and having a health promotion and preventive approach. Mention is made of the fact that people can be educated as to which is the most appropriate level of care to access at any particular time. This approach would ideally reduce unnecessary over-dependence on conventional services and 'the pill for every ill' attitude while encouraging appropriate presentation for screening and preventive services and early detection. There was emphasis also on culturally appropriate messages and locations; integration – a multidisciplinary approach, where appropriate, in one building; more staff – GPs, public health nurses, counsellors, other therapists (e.g. speech therapists, occupational therapists, physiotherapists), social workers, community health workers; valuing complementary therapies alongside conventional healthcare approaches; and having a community development approach (see under crosscutting issues for reference to community development). The latter was defined as being about people working collectively for social change which will improve the quality of their lives, the communities in which they live or the society of which they are part. It is about enabling and empowering those who are disadvantaged to identify and articulate need, to participate in working for change and to influence decision-making structures that affect them, their communities and the wider society.

Community-based supports/continuing care

The focus here was on: older people, people with disabilities, people with mental health needs, carers, homeless people. Suggestions included the following: local services to support people and their carers in their own homes; additional day care; more respite care; more financial and societal recognition and support for carers and a more streamlined home help service. There was a recommendation that maximum waiting times be set for community supports and that these should be designated as core services. There were also calls for more long-term residential places for those for whom care in the community was not (or no longer) an option. There were calls for the implementation of a dementia care plan and also for special attention to homeless people in general but particularly those with addiction problems.

Acute hospital care

Concerns expressed in relation to acute hospital care related mainly to waiting lists and length of wait for inpatient care; the inequity of the two-tier waiting system for in-patient services whereby private patients are fast-tracked for care; lack of transparency in relation to waiting list/times; waiting times in A&E; centralisation of services (particularly for cancer patients and for children); inadequate availability of senior clinical decision makers. Suggestions for improving access included the following: increasing the number of beds; having a clear admittance policy, i.e. medical need and place in the queue, not wealth; abolishing the two-tier system;

increasing the proportion of day cases; having more 'step-down' facilities; having a consultant-provided service; monitoring use of public resources by private practice; introducing economic pricing of private beds; having a radical restructuring of non-emergencies in A&E, directing them to primary care; streamlining appointments and organising them in a way which takes more account of patients' needs.

Crosscutting issues

A number of what might be termed crosscutting issues were emphasised in submissions. These are crosscutting in that, in most cases, they are relevant across the spectrum of healthcare polices and services and, in many cases, are relevant to the other public policies which affect health. These include:

- Consultation/participation

- A community development approach

- Access to information on services, rights and entitlements in a way which acknowledges diversity in society

- Sensitivity/communications training for staff

- Flexible hours of service and client-friendly premises

- Geographic access

- Integration of policies and services and 'joined up' working

- Funding

- Proofing mechanisms

Consultation/participation in decision-making

There was a widely expressed view that if citizens, communities, local communities, patients and their families, carers and providers (both statutory and voluntary) are engaged and involved in decision-making processes, a more flexible and needs-based approach will emerge that will support people's health. These consultations need to be ongoing and taking place at local and community level.

Community Development approach

Several submissions, including the composite submission from the Community and Voluntary Pillar, made a call for consultation and participation in the context of a community development approach with an emphasis on engaging the energies and assets of local communities as the basis of any programme to tackle health inequalities. It is considered that this would give people a greater sense of ownership of their health and of health and related services. It is stated that health board policies and action in relation to social development, community development and other partnership activities must be endorsed, supported and resourced. Community development was defined as being about people working collectively for social change which will improve the quality of their lives, the communities in which they live or the society of which they are part. It is about enabling and empowering those who are disadvantaged to identify and articulate need, to participate in working for change and to influence decision making structures that affect them, their communities and wider society. There was strong support for strengthening community action for health through incorporating community development approaches into health work and incorporating public health work into community development. Reference was made to the stronger focus on community development and health in Northern Ireland and how Ireland should be following this way of working, in particular through the development of a community development and health network.

Access to information on services, rights and entitlements which acknowledges diversity in society

Making information available and accessible to citizens and communities, particularly those who are most in need of it, is outlined as an important way of improving people's ability to access and use the services and benefits to which they are entitled. Suggestions included involving excluded groups themselves in the development and dissemination of materials; making information more accessible to people with low literacy; making information available in simple jargon free English and, where relevant, in other languages; better use of information technology; making use of existing networks and channels of communication for circulating information; a more enthusiastic and proactive approach by staff to giving information; assistance with form filling and in the context of a multicultural society paying particular attention to issues of ethnicity and race.

Sensitivity/communications training for staff

Training for professionals and staff working in health and other public services, in particular sensitising them to issues faced by people who are living in poverty or experiencing social exclusion, was recommended as another key factor in making services accessible and appropriate. This was mentioned in particular in relation to Travellers, other ethnic minorities, people with disabilities, gay, lesbian and bisexual people. Suggestions made include provision at regular intervals of awareness and sensitivity training to healthcare providers on issues of gender, ethnicity, race, sexual orientation and economic disadvantage and the relationship between social factors and health status.

Flexible hours of service and client-friendly premises

There were several calls for provision of services during more flexible hours. There were also a number of references to the need for client-friendly premises. Suggestions included reception areas easily accessible for small children; confidential consulting rooms; 'access rooms' for the non-residential parent in lone parent families; wheelchair access and crèche facilities so that parents can avail of a number of services, including health services.

Geographic Access

Reference has already been made to this issue in the paragraph on transport in the section on public policy. Suggestions for improvements included: providing services locally where possible and appropriate; more outreach services and mobile clinics; improved transport and associated supports – vouchers, B&B expenses and better co-ordination of appointments with local transport.

Integration of policies and services, and 'joined up' working

A large number of submissions drew attention to the need for greater integration of public policies and services both within the health sector and between that sector and other sectors. e.g. environment and housing, education, social, community and family affairs, statutory and voluntary sectors. The point was made that many sectors and disciplines currently work in isolation from each other. Integration was felt to be particularly important for vulnerable groups, e.g. people with mental health needs, homeless people, Travellers, refugees and asylum seekers and people experiencing multiple discrimination.

It was also emphasised that this 'joined-up' working needs to be 'bottom up' as much as 'top down,' and mechanisms need to be put in place to enable these to meet. Initiatives such as the local drugs task forces, Partnerships for Youth Health and the Integrated Services Projects are cited as models which can provide learning for the development of effective 'joined up' work. Funding mechanisms need to support this intersectoral and intrasectoral working and there was particular mention that joint funding of projects at local level is required. Budget holding responsibilities would strengthen local partnership arrangements.

The importance of multidisciplinary working within the health sector itself was emphasised. Better communication between GPs and public health nurses was specifically mentioned as were closer links between community care and hospitals. There is reference to the need for introducing a systematic approach to knowledge management which would integrate patient information between all relevant personnel - within data protection guidelines - as a cost efficiency measure.

Funding of health services

A few submissions addressed the matter of funding and the issue is implicit in many of the calls for improvement in services in other submissions. Points made include: the need for increased funding; the need for a more flexible funding system that supports meaningful change and facilitates more dynamic and creative ways of working, e.g. intersectoral working; the current funding system reflects fiscal imperatives rather than the realistic time scale required to implement health strategies and see measurable health gain - annual funding cycles make it too easy to withdraw funding; while health gain should be the principal deciding factor for introduction of health strategies, cost effectiveness and cost utility are also important and a public policy is only as good as the resources which back it up. A number of other submissions made the general comment that the system of funding of health services needed to be reviewed.

Policy proofing mechanisms

A range of proofing mechanisms was recommended in the submissions - from equality and anti-discrimination proofing to the proofing of other policies for their impact on health. Health impact assessment with health equity impact assessment as a core component was referred to in many submissions as one essential way of developing healthier public policies. Rationalising the various proofing mechanisms, e.g. poverty proofing, gender proofing, equality proofing was also mentioned and a suggestion was made that many, if not all, of these could be integrated under an overarching equality proofing mechanism.

Information and research

There was acknowledgement in a large number of submissions of the dearth of information and research on which to set, monitor and review NAPS targets for health. Recommendations included the following: identify existing gaps (many gaps were mentioned in the submissions); disaggregate data on health status, access and outcomes by relevant subgroups; modify existing surveys to capture data on relevant subgroups; have qualitative as well as quantitative measures; have research and information on social determinants and social indicators, as well as on the traditional medical measures of mortality and morbidity and finally use a consultation and partnership approach in research and information activities.

Conclusion

The issues outlined above are the key themes which emerged in the submissions. The emphasis placed on them suggests that addressing them is widely viewed as the way forward in tackling issues of poverty, social exclusion and inequalities in health. Many more detailed points were made in relation to the needs of specific vulnerable groups which it is not possible to outline in this document. Information on these is available in the more detailed *Report of the Consultation Process for Working Group on NAPS and Health* which is available from the Institute of Public Health, 6 Kildare St, Dublin 2 (Phone 6629287).

PART 6

Key themes emerging from the consultation process

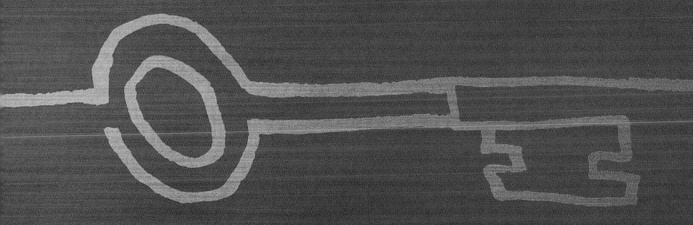

Introduction

The consultative process associated with the development of the Health Strategy *Quality and Fairness - A Health System for You* was the most comprehensive effort ever made in this country to gather the views of those with an interest in the future development of the health system. The process involved actively seeking the views of

- The general public (through calls for submissions and the commissioning of market research)

- Organisations

- Health boards (members, management and staff)

- Staff of the Department of Health and Children

- The National Anti-Poverty Strategy (NAPS).

The aim of this concluding section is to draw out some of the themes that run through the submissions and integrate the complex range of views and ideas emerging from them. The selection and presentation of these themes reflect the views of the authors as to the core themes that seem to link the various reports. These observations are not intended, in any sense, to serve as a summary or prioritisation of the material in the reports. To attempt such a task would undermine the integrity of each of the reports and the effort made to facilitate the emergence of the wide range of perspectives within each of the sectors.

The Irish context

Irish society has undergone major changes, particularly in the last decade. These include:

- The increased prosperity of the country; a major reservation here, however, is that all sections of society are not benefiting equally from the economic boom and that social exclusion remains a significant problem for many people across the country

- The increased diversity within Irish society and growing multiculturalism; while many welcome the new diversity, it poses a fundamental challenge for health service provision

- The changes that are taking place in terms of demography and family structure have major implications for the development of the health services.

The reports stress that in devising the Health Strategy, full account must be taken of such developments.

A 'whole-system' approach to health

Achieving best health for all is seen in the consultation processes as a complex and multi-faceted challenge, involving individuals and communities, as well as policy makers and service providers.

The role of health policy and health services goes beyond care and treatment, to encompass the task of advocating a public policy of which health is at the core.

High priority is given to the promotion of health and prevention of illness, but this needs to happen in a way that empowers individuals and communities to take responsibility for their lives and their health and which provides the supports they need for that task. Health promotion and illness prevention cannot be compartmentalised within a narrow 'health' focus but must be viewed broadly, encompassing education, housing, income support, provision for leisure, mental well-being, as well as complex structural issues such as poverty and marginalisation.

The challenge of promoting personal and community empowerment for healthy living is especially central to the health and well-being of deprived and marginalised individuals and communities. The feedback also underscores the strategic and long-term benefits of giving children and young people the information, facilities and supports needed to optimise their health and well-being.

Going beyond 'more'

The need for more investment at all levels of health and health services is a theme that inevitably emerges from all facets of the consultation process. The focus is on the need for more personnel in every area of healthcare, more hospital beds, more capital and revenue funding, investment in infrastructural programmes such as education, training, research, buildings, equipment and information technology.

However, it is also clear from the consultation that the desired change is not only about more resources. There is a push for significant strategic changes in policy and practice. The strategic changes proposed seem to crystallise around how the health system is experienced by the public. The changes envisaged embody concepts of holistic and seamless health systems, a refocusing on community, fairness and equity of access to services, the quality of care and the quality of people's experience of the health system.

Towards a holistic and seamless service

A strong strategic focus is on a health system which is responsive to the whole person and their well-being. A health system built on this 'whole-person' approach would respond to people's personal, family, social, economic and cultural circumstances. So, agencies and personnel must integrate their work and they must be informed and sensitive to the wider circumstances of the person presenting for service. A key theme in this person-centred vision is that of flexibility – flexibility in professional practice, in service availability, in ability to perceive the 'bigger picture' within which individuals seek care, treatment or support. There is a clear understanding also that system rigidities – in attitudes, contractual arrangements, service delivery systems, boundaries between agencies and funding mechanisms – must be addressed if the new person-centred ethos is to permeate the health system.

People expect that concerted effort will be expended towards planning and delivering a co-ordinated and integrated health service where good practice in one area is not undermined by blockages in another. What is also essential is that health and well-being are not viewed as being the sole responsibility of the Department of Health and Children but that all national and local agencies as well as individuals would work towards identifying and playing their part in developing a healthier society.

A focus on community

Another facet of the shift in strategic thinking highlighted by the consultation process is the case made for investment in healthy and caring communities. This thinking is evident at many levels. It is evident in the calls for a refocusing of the health system towards care in the community; it comes through in the many proposals for a new model of an accessible community-based health centre, capable of meeting a much wider range of needs; it can be seen in the emphasis on developing the general practitioner service in various ways.

The focus on community is strongly evident too in the priority given to the need to provide support, care and treatment within their own communities and families for vulnerable people including older people, people with disabilities and people experiencing mental health problems.

The need for rural transport is highlighted consistently. Services should come to people in isolated communities. Professionals should visit people in their homes. Community hospitals should be equipped to serve many more needs at local level. Acute hospitals should have strong linkages with the professional personnel in the communities served by the hospitals.

It is also clear that the health of communities needs to benefit from increased state support at many levels; informal carers need many kinds of help from the State; health professionals need new kinds of structures, working arrangements and buildings. Many more community-based health professionals are needed in virtually every category.

The shift towards community is not seen as taking place at the 'expense' of acute care. The difficult balance that needs to be struck between widespread local access to a range of health services, and the maintenance of high quality national or regional specialisms is highlighted. Stronger community-based provision is seen as enabling hospitals and specialists to target their resources to those in need of acute care, while at the same time fostering a stronger culture of personal and local responsibility for positive and preventive health.

A fair health system

It emerged from all of the consultation reports that there is a strong will to change what is perceived as an inequitable system, most particularly in the case of access to hospital treatment and specialist care. Other less publicly debated inequities concern the limitations on care choices for certain groups, for example, people with medical cards, people living on the islands and homeless people with mental health difficulties. Inequalities arising from geographic disparities in services were also a source of concern.

Fairness and equity are not seen as meaning that the same level of service is provided for all. Groups with additional needs warrant a high priority. The submissions call for greatly enhanced services for vulnerable groups, especially older people and people with mental health difficulties. Marginalised and deprived communities, ethnic minorities and homeless people are among those seen in the consultation reports as also warranting priority.

Fairness will also necessitate ensuring that services are geared up to meet the distinct needs of women, men, children and teenagers.

Additional health service capacity, through higher levels of staffing and resources is a key part of the solution that is envisaged to the challenge of providing an equitable service, as well as changes in entitlements to free healthcare.

Delivering high quality of care, treatment and support

The future development of the health system must put a very high premium on the quality of the service provided. The quality agenda is concerned with good outcomes for service users. Quality is also linked in strong measure to people's personal experience of the health service and health service personnel. So, the quality agenda is expressed through calls for more flexible services, appointment arrangements that respect the demands on people's time, the need for child and adolescent-friendly services and many similar user-centred services.

Members of the public focus mainly on their expectations for quality services to the individual. Organisations and service providers go beyond that to underscore the need for systems that can embed quality into service delivery – quality development programmes, systems to audit both professional and agency standards, staff and management training, data gathering for monitoring and evaluation and research.

Quality is also seen as linked intrinsically to capacity within services in terms of staffing and facilities.

Respectful relationships

The theme of respectful relationships is evident in the consultation process. Organisations and the public see a need for great sensitivity among healthcare workers towards individuals, especially when those individuals are vulnerable, on account of old age, illness, poverty or cultural difference.

Reported experiences of disrespect or poor communication appear to make a strong and lasting impact on individuals. This sense of hurt is balanced by an understanding of the many pressures on health service personnel and by many statements of appreciation for the dedication, professionalism and commitment of health service staff.

Structural developments are put forward that could help to build relationships of mutual respect and trust and to support people when things go wrong. These include training and development programmes for health service personnel in customer service, effective complaints and appeals procedures, anti-ageism and disability awareness programmes, culturally sensitive information services and practices, as well as the building up of staffing levels.

Mutual respect is also seen as essential in the relationships between the groups who make up the health system; service providers, service users, advocacy groups, policy makers, funders, staff and employers. The consultation process highlights the expectation that all those stakeholders will have a continuing role in shaping the future of the health system through national, regional and local partnerships and permanent consultative structures.

The other significant strand of this theme of respectful relationships is the emphasis on supporting the personnel of the health services through a human resources strategy. This strategy is expected to develop a coherent and longer-term programme for recruitment, training, working arrangements, pay and industrial relations and should place high priority on promoting the well-being of health service personnel.

Conclusion

There are high expectations for the Health Strategy and much goodwill towards it among those who contributed to the consultation processes. It is seen as urgently needed, as well as timely from the perspective of public finances.

The expectation is that the Health Strategy will construct a cohesive, multi-faceted policy framework for the task of optimising the health of the nation. It is also expected to deliver, in due course, a health system which is fair, accessible, people-centred and quality-driven.

It seems that in order to deliver such a person-centred, fair and responsive health service, it is no longer enough to talk about 'the health service' as a single, undifferentiated service for a majority, with some 'add-on' features to meet special needs. Rather, the consultation points towards a mainstream service that is structured and resourced to meet a complex mix of needs and resources in every community.

New ways of working, strong partnerships and teamwork at every level and between every level of service are expected to be the hallmark of the health system of the future. The design of support systems for these new and complex relationships will pose a challenge for all those charged with managing implementation.

Although the contributors to the consultation process do not quantify the level of resources needed to deliver on the vision they hold for the new Strategy, it is clear that the expectation is for major investment of resources in the coming years to achieve the quality and level of health service that people want.

Appendices

Appendix 1

Members of Project Team sub-group and health board co-ordinators

Project Team sub-group members

Ms Mary Dowling
Assistant Principal Officer
Department of Health and Children

Ms Siobhán Kennan
Assistant Principal Officer
Department of Health and Children

Dr Ambrose McLoughlin
Deputy Chief Executive Officer
North Eastern Health Board, Kells, Co Meath

Co-ordinators for the Health Board Consultation Process

Mr Tom Beegan
Deputy Chief Executive Officer
South Eastern Health Board, Lacken, Dublin Road, Kilkenny

Dr Seán Conroy
Regional Manager, Corporate Affairs and Population Health
Western Health Board, Merlin Park Hospital, Galway

Mr James Conway
Assistant Chief Executive Officer
Mid-Western Health Board, 31-33 Catherine Street, Limerick

Ms Anne Doherty
Director of Strategy and Planning
Southern Health Board, Wilton Road, Cork

Ms Bernie Hyland
Health Promotion Officer
North Western Health Board, Manorhamilton, Co Leitrim

Mr John Lamont
Assistant Chief Executive, Planning and Development
Northern Area Health Board, Unit 7, Swords Business Campus, Balheary Road, Swords, Co Dublin

Mr Kevin McCarthy
Assistant Chief Executive, Planning and Development
East Coast Area Health Board, Southern Cross House, Southern Cross Business Park, Boghall Road, Bray, Co Wicklow

Mr Seosamh Ó Maolalaí
Co- Ordinator Health Services National Partnership Forum
63-64 Adelaide Road, Dublin 2

Ms Eileen O' Neill
Project Specialist, Children and Families
Midland Health Board, Arden Road, Tullamore, Co Offaly

Ms Martina Queally
Director of Health Promotion
South Western Area Health Board, City Gate, St Augustine Street, Dublin 8

Ms Patricia Smith
Senior Human Resource Officer
Eastern Regional Health Authority, Mill Lane, Palmerstown, Dublin 20

Mr Larry Walsh
Assistant Chief Executive Officer, Governance and Planning
North Eastern Health Board, Kells, Co Meath

Appendix 2

The consultation pack *'Your Views about Health'*

HEALTH STRATEGY 2001

DEPARTMENT OF HEALTH AND CHILDREN
AN ROINN
SLÁINTE
AGUS LEANAÍ

A New Health Strategy

The Minister for Health and Children, Micheál Martin, T.D., his Department and the Health Boards, are working on a major new plan, **Health Strategy 2001.** The purpose of this Strategy is to develop health and personal social services over the next 5-7 years to meet your health needs and the needs of your family.

Health Strategy 2001 will be designed to provide a health system which:

- Is fair
- Is there when you need it
- Gives the best possible quality of service to people
- Gives people a say in planning services
- Helps those most in need
- Aims to prevent illness
- Encourages people to look after their own health

HEALTH MATTERS TO EVERYONE

The task of making sure that everyone living in Ireland has the best possible health is a major challenge for a lot of people and agencies.

It is a personal challenge for each of us, because we make choices every day that affect our health.

It is a very big challenge for the Department of Health and Children, the health boards, and all those who provide health services.

There are many other organisations and agencies whose work makes a difference to our health, for example, local authorities, schools, sporting organisations.

The work of many other Government Departments has an impact on health, in areas such as income support, road safety, workplace health and safety, the environment, housing and leisure facilities. The Social Partners also play an important part - employer organisations, trade unions, farming bodies, the voluntary and community sector.

Please let us have your views and proposals for ways of ensuring best health and well being for everyone.

You have a chance to influence how money is spent on health services and what is given priority.

WHAT DO THE HEALTH SERVICES DO?
WHO USES HEALTH SERVICES?

Everyone uses the health services at some time. The Department of Health and Children, together with the health boards and other agencies, is responsible for a wide range of health and personal social services. These include:

Community Services:
- Community nursing, general practitioner services, out-patient clinics.

Hospital Services
- In-patient, day and out-patient services provided in a hospital setting such as acute hospitals, maternity hospitals, psychiatric hospitals and district/community hospitals.

Children
- Child health services
- Services for children considered to be at risk of abuse and neglect

Services for Older People
- Nursing homes and day centres
- Palliative Care

Services for people with an intellectual, physical or sensory disability
- Residential, day and respite care services
- Home support services including personal assistance

Mental Health Services
- Integration programmes for persons receiving long-stay institutional care
- Suicide Reduction/Prevention Strategies
- Child and Adolescent Psychiatric Services

Entitlements to Health Services
- Medical Cards and Community Drugs Scheme

Personal Social Services
- Home Helps
- Social work services
- Support for voluntary organisations

Health Promotion/Prevention Services
- Anti-Smoking and Alcohol Awareness Campaigns
- Screening and immunisation programmes
- Cancer and Cardiovascular Strategies

This is not intended to be a complete list. It gives an idea of the range and variety of the health services.

ABOUT THE QUESTIONS

Please note the range of services that make up the health services.

Question 1 asks for your views about any recent experience you have had of the health services.

If you have had a good experience, we would like to know what was good about that experience, so that good practices can be built on in the future. If you had a bad experience, we would like to know what was it about your experience that was bad, so that we can look at the need for changes in practices.

Questions 2, 3 and 4.

Here are some possible areas you might find helpful when responding to these questions.

- Are there new kinds of health services needed?
- Do we need to look at where services are located?
- Are there changes that would make services more user-friendly?
- Do we need changes in the way services are organised?
- Do we need changes in entitlements for some services?
- Do we need changes in lifestyles?
- Do we need new legislation?
- Are there some special groups that need extra help in order to be healthy? What do you think they need?
- What else would help people who care for older relatives?
- Is there some other action that should be taken by Government Departments other than the Department of Health and Children, to promote best health and wellbeing?
- Is there, perhaps, some way that people themselves should get support to take responsibilty for their own health, or the health of their family?

Members of the Public

Please use the consultation form "**Your Views about Health**" to give us your views. There is no need to answer every question – just those that are important to you. You can use the form that is supplied, or if you want to give your views on computer, use the form on our website.

You may want to get together with a group of friends or neighbours to talk about health issues, and share views, before you send us "**Your Views About Health**".

At the end of the consultation form, we ask for some personal information. The purpose is to check if we are getting a good spread of views from different parts of the country and different age-groups. While this information will be helpful, you are not required to give it.

Organisations

We would like to hear from organisations and groups working in areas that are directly related to health.

We also want to hear from organisations and groups whose activities have a bearing on people's health and well being, such as sporting groups, arts organisations, and the wide range of groups working to improve people's quality of life and sense of well-being.

We would like to have the view of your particular organisation on the changes needed to promote best health. We want to know what your organisation sees as the priorities for change and development and for health spending, so as to ensure best health and well being for people living in Ireland in the coming years.

Returning the Consultation Form

We need your views by the 27th April. You may return the consultation form by post in the enclosed stamped addressed envelope. Alternatively you may download a copy from our website. This can be returned to us by e-mail to healthstrategy2001@health.irlgov.ie or by post to:

"Your Views About Health"
Department of Health and Children
Second Floor, Hawkins House,
FREEPOST, Dublin 2.
(no stamp needed)

HELPFUL INFORMATION

There are several pieces of helpful background information about the Strategy on the Department of Health and Children website:
http://www.doh.ie/hstrat/index.html

The National Anti-Poverty Strategy (NAPS)

The National Anti-Poverty Strategy (NAPS) is a Government initiative to end poverty and social exclusion. If you have views on how the health of people living in poverty can get special support, you should check this website for information about a special consultation on that subject: http://www.doh.ie/naps

---

Submissions may be released under the Freedom of Information Act, 1997.

CONSULTATION FORM

YOUR VIEWS ABOUT HEALTH
Tell us What <u>You</u> Think is Important

**DEPARTMENT
OF HEALTH
AND CHILDREN**
AN ROINN
SLÁINTE
AGUS LEANAÍ

Please read Health Strategy 2001, the information leaflet enclosed with this form before answering the questions. If you don't have enough space please attach extra pages to the form when you are returning it.

---

1. Have your recent experiences of health services been good or bad or mixed?
   (Please tick box)

Good ☐   Bad ☐   Mixed ☐

Can you tell us more about what made your experiences good or bad?

_____

_____

_____

_____

_____

_____

_____

_____

_____

_____

_____

_____

_____

_____

_____

_____

_____

2. What changes would have the greatest benefit for people's health and well-being, in your opinion?

    (When writing your answer please start with what you think is the most important change and if possible give five changes in order of preference)

Change1

Change 2

Change 3

Change 4

Change 5

3. If extra money was to be invested in health and well-being, what should
    the priorities be for spending that money?

4. Have you any other views or proposals for the new Health Strategy?

The following section is for classification purposes only.

1. **Is this submission from:**

(a) An individual ☐

(b) A family ☐

(c) A health service worker ☐

(d) An organisation directly connected with health/health services ☐

    Name of organisation: ....

(e) An organisation not directly connected with health services ☐

    Name of organisation: ....

Individual submissions (It would be very useful if you could give us some information about yoursef)

2. **Gender (Please tick box)**

Male ☐

Female ☐

3. **Age (Please tick box)**

12 and Under ☐		40 - 49 ☐
13 - 19 ☐		50- 59 ☐
20 - 29 ☐		60 - 69 ☐
30 - 39 ☐		70 and Over ☐

4. **Where you live (Please tick box)**

Urban Area ☐

Rural Area ☐

The County you live in: ....

If you would like us to send you an acknowledgement of your submission you may wish to give us your name and address:

Name: ....

Address: ....

....

....

....

Appendix 3

Submissions from organisations

There were over 300 submissions from organisations. These included:

Accord, Co Louth
Accord, Co Mayo
Active Retired Association, Limerick
Acupuncture and Chinese Medicine Organisation
Adelaide Hospital Society
Age & Opportunity
Age Action Ireland
Alliance Homecare Services
Alzheimer Society of Ireland
Alzheimer Society of Ireland (North Cork Branch)
AMEN
An Bord Altranais
Anchor Treatment Centre Ltd.
Arklow & District healthcare and Facilities Improvement Committee
Arklow and District Asthma Society
ASH Ireland
Association of Health Boards in Ireland
Association of Health Education/Health Promotion Officers in Ireland
Association of Hospital Chief Executives
Association of Optometrists, Ireland
Asthma Society of Ireland
Aware
Aware (Ennis Branch)
Baby Friendly Hospital Initiative Working Group, Galway
Ballincollig Family Centre
Banada Development Agency Ltd
Band Three Directors of Nursing
Bandon Community Hospital
Barnardos
Barnardos (Mid-West Branch)
Beara Action Group
Beaumont Hospital
Blarney Care of the Aged
Bodywhys (Central Office)
Bodywhys (Limerick Branch)
Bon Secours Health System
Bridges Droichid
BUPA Ireland
Cancer Support Group, Donegal
Canteen
Care Alliance Ireland
CARI Foundation, Limerick

Caring for Carers Ireland

Carnew Community Care

Castlebar Soroptimist Club

Castlehaven Nursing Association

Castletownbere Community Care and Housing Association Ltd.

Cavan County Council

Centre for Nursing, Midwifery and healthcare Studies, Tralee

Centre for Sport Science and Health, Dublin City University

Cherry Orchard Family Care Centre

Cheshire Foundation in Ireland

Children in Hospital Ireland

Children's Rights Alliance

Citizens Information Centre, Wexford

Clare Mental Health Services

Clondalkin Partnership

Clondalkin Travellers Development Group

Clondalkin Travellers Primary healthcare Project

Clondalkin Women's Network

Cluain Mhuire St John of God Adult Community Mental Health Service (Management Team)

CoAction West Cork

Coeliac Society of Ireland

Combat Poverty Agency

Comhairle

Comhairle na nOspidéal

Comhar

Comhdháil Oileáin na hÉireann

Comhlamh (Health and Development Group)

Community Connections, Cavan

Community Development Project, Bantry

Community Mothers Programme

Community and Voluntary Pillar

Community Workers Co-Operative

Consultants in Old Age Psychiatry in Ireland

Consultative Council on Hepatitis C

Consumers Association of Ireland

Continence Promotion Unit, Eastern Regional Health Boards

Cork Advocacy Network

Cork Association of Parents and Friends of the Mentally Handicapped

Cork Lupus Support Group

Cork Mental Health Association

Cork Tinnitus Support Group

Cork Women's Right to Choose Group

Council for Children's Hospitals' Care

Country Club Meet and Train Group Limerick

Cumann Cabhrach na Sean, Kerry

Dean Maxwell Community Nursing Unit (Residents and Attenders Group)

Dental Council

Department of Health Services Management, Trinity College, Dublin

Department of Preventive Medicine and Health Promotion, St. Vincent's University Hospital, Dublin

Derry Healthy Cities Project

Derrybeg Care of the Aged Committee

Diabetes Federation of Ireland

Disability Federation of Ireland

Disability Information Project

Dóchas
Donegal Carers Association
Donegal Town Women's Group
Donegal Women's Network
Doora Mother and Toddler Group
Drogheda Community Services
Dublin Rape Crisis Centre
Dunmanway Active Retirement Group
East Clare Youthreach
Eastern Vocational Enterprises Ltd. (Eve Holdings)
Eastern Vocational Enterprise Ltd. (Larine Court Resource Centre - Staff Submission)
Eastern Vocational Enterprises Ltd. (New Dawn Training Centre)
Empowerment of Nurses and Midwives Steering Group
Equality Authority
Europa Donna Ireland
European Cross Border Taxation Group
Faculty of Health Sciences, Trinity College, Dublin
Families and Friends Association of Scoil Mochua
Family Resource Centre, Limerick
Fatima Mansions Task Group
Festina Lente Foundation
Fibromyalgia Support Group, Cork
Fine Gael Women's Network (Health Panel)
Fingal Development Board (Health and Social Services Working Group)
Friends of Ennistymon Hospital
Galway Lesbian Line
Good Shepherd Services, Cork
Headway Ireland
Health and Safety Authority
Health Research Board
Health Services Employers Agency
Heart Children Ireland
Holywell Trust Support Agency
Hope Project, Cork
Hospital Pharmacists Association Ireland
Hospitaller Order of Saint John of God
IMPACT
IMPACT (Clinical Engineering Professional and Vocational Group)
Inishowen Learning Disability Network
Institute of Community Health Nursing
Institute of Public Health in Ireland
Institution of Engineers of Ireland
IPA Health Sector Advisory Group
Irish Aids and Mobility Network
Irish Association for Counselling and Therapy
Irish Association of Dermatologists Manpower Committee
Irish Association of Health Stores
Irish Association of Medical Herbalists
Irish Association of Older People
Irish Blood Transfusion Service
Irish Commission for Prisoners Overseas
Irish Countrywomen's Association (Health and Social Affairs Committee)
Irish Countrywomen's Association (Dunmanway Branch)
Irish Fostercare Association (Limerick Branch)

Irish Health Services Management Institute
Irish Health Trade Association
Irish Heart Foundation
Irish Heart Foundation Council on Stroke
Irish Hospice Foundation
Irish Kidney Association
Irish Lymphoedema Support Network
Irish ME/CFS Support Group
Irish Medical Organisation
Irish Medicines Board
Irish National Council of ADHD Support Groups
Irish National Council of ADHD Support Groups (South East Branch)
Irish Nurses Organisation
Irish Nurses Organisation (Care of the Elderly Section)
Irish Nursing Homes Organisation Ltd.
Irish Nutrition and Dietetic Institute
Irish Pharmaceutical Healthcare Association
Irish Pharmaceutical Union
Irish Practice Nurses Association
Irish Refugee Council
Irish School of Homeopathy
Irish Sleep Apnoea Trust
Irish Society for the Prevention of Cruelty to Children
Irish Society of Chartered Physiotherapists
Irish Society of Homeopaths
Irish Society of Physicians in Geriatric Medicine
Irish Sports Council
Irish Wheelchair Association
Irish Wheelchair Association (Clare Branch)
Kerry Care Foundation
Killorglin Community Pre-School
Knocknacarra Active Retirement Association
Lacken Community Care
Laois Centre for Independent Living
Leitrim Association of People with Disabilities
Lifestart Family Centre
Longford Active Retirement Association
Maharishi Vedic Approach to Health
Mater Misericordiae Hospital, Dublin
Matrons/Nurse Managers, Elderly Care Services (Mid-Western Health Board)
Meath Centre for Independent Living
Meath Women's Refuge
Medical Council
Medical Laboratory Scientists Association
Mental Health Association of Ireland
MGI/Air Products Medical Ireland
Mid-West Parents of Deaf Children
Midwifery Tutor Group
Midwives Association of Ireland
Migraine Association of Ireland
Monaghan Community Mental Health Team
Mount Merrion Community Care Committee
Mountview/Blakestown Community Drugs Team
Muintir na Tire (Cork County Federation)

National Association for Deaf People

National Association for the Mentally Handicapped of Ireland (NAMHI)

National Association of Hospital Chaplains

National Association of Ovulation Method of Ireland Ltd (NAOMI)

National Association of Widows in Ireland

National Council for the Blind of Ireland

National Council for the Professional Development of Nursing and Midwifery

National Council on Ageing and Older People

National Disability Authority

National Disease Surveillance Centre

National Federation of Voluntary Bodies providing Services to People with Mental Handicap

National Infertility Support and Information Group

National Midwifery Advisory Forum

National Rehabilitation Hospital, Dublin

National Suicide Review Group

National Women's Council of Ireland

National Youth Council of Ireland

Nenagh Community Services

Network Rape Crisis Centres

Neurofibromatosis Association of Ireland

Neurological Alliance

North Leitrim and West Cavan Carers Group

North Leitrim Men's Group Ltd

Northside Traveller Support Group

Nurse Continence Advisors Forum

Occupational Health Nurses Association of Ireland

Office for Health Management

Office of Tobacco Control

Pathways Research Group, Schizophrenia Ireland (Galway Branch)

Patient Focus

Pavee Point

Peggy Carty School of Deportment

People with Disabilities in Ireland Ltd.

Pharmaceutical Society of Ireland

Phrenz Support Group

Portiuncula Hospital (Directorate of Care Group)

Positive Action

Post Polio Support Group

Postgraduate Medical and Dental Board

Psychiatric Nurses' Association of Ireland

Psychological Society of Ireland

Reception and Integration Agency, Department of Justice, Equality and Law Reform

Regional Health Promotion Managers/ Directors of Health Promotion Group

RehabCare Service Users, Bray

RehabCare, Sligo (National Representative Advisory Council of Ireland)

Resource Centre for Elderly, Cork

Resource House Project, Sligo

Royal College of Physicians of Ireland

Royal College of Physicians of Ireland (Faculty of Occupational Medicine)

Royal College of Physicians of Ireland (Faculty of Paediatrics)

Royal College of Physicians of Ireland (Faculty of Public Health Medicine)

Royal College of Physicians (Institute of Obstetricians and Gynaecologists)

Royal College of Psychiatrists

Royal College of Surgeons in Ireland

i165535324

Ruhama Women's Project
Rural Community Care Network, Limerick and North Cork
St. Catherine's Aid Society
St. Columbus C.N.U.
St. James's Hospital, Dublin
St. Joseph's Association for the Mentally Handicapped, Portrane
St. Joseph's Ladies Club
St. Michael's House (Parents Future Planning Group)
St. Michael's House (Occupational Therapy Department)
St. Munchin's Community Development Project
St. Senan's Senior Citizens Group, Co Cork
Schizophrenia Ireland
Sensory Disability Access
Services for Elderly Forum, Co Galway
Simon Community of Ireland
SIPTU
Sláinte Pobal
Sligo Social Services Council Ltd
Smoking Target Action Group (STAG)
Social Workers in Child Psychiatry
Society of St. Vincent de Paul
Southwest Kerry Women's Association
Stepping Stones, Galway
Stillorgan Information & Support Cancer Service
Stoma Support Group (Sligo Branch)
Strokestown Social Service Council
Summerhill Active Retirement Group
Tallaght Mental Health Service
Templemore Women's Group
Three Dublin Maternity Hospitals (Joint Standing Committee)
Thurles Carer Support Group
Tipperary Centre for Independent Living Ltd.
Tir Boghaine Teo, Donegal
Traveller Health Unit, Western Health Board
Trust
Urostomy Association
VHI Healthcare
Vietnamese Irish Association
Virginia's Health Studios
Waterside House Women's Refuge
West Limerick Independent Living Ltd
Western Neurosurgery Campaign
Wexford Disability Development Ltd.
Willowdale Day Hospital
Women's Aid
Women's Health Council
Working Group on Code of Practice for Sheltered Work
Yoga Therapy Ireland
Youth Initiative in Partnership

In addition to the above, a number of organisations participated in the consultative process undertaken by the health boards. The full reports of the various boards can be obtained directly from the headquarters of each board or via the relevant board's website